ANCHOR'S AWEIGH

The Story of
David Glasgow Farragut

BY JEAN LEE LATHAM

Illustrations by Eros Keith

HARPER & ROW, PUBLISHERS
NEW YORK, EVANSTON, AND LONDON

ACM

Author's Note

In the days of square-riggers, getting a ship under way was like starting a stick-shift car parked facing up a hill. The anchor was the brake; the wind in the sails was the engine. The cry "Anchor's aweigh" meant the anchor was out of the ground. In other words the brake was released; the wind must fill the sails and move the ship.

The song "Anchor's Aweigh" goes back to about the time of the War of 1812. It was a song of farewell which began:

Oh, the anchor's aweigh! The anchor's aweigh!
Farewell, fare-you-well, my own true love!

CONTENTS

ANCHOR'S AWEIGH

1. SON OF A FOREIGNER

Glasgow was going-on-six before he knew that his father was different—before the day he heard the woman whispering. Until that day his father had seemed like all the other fathers, only braver and more fun.

Lots of fathers had fought in the Revolutionary War and helped America beat the British, but his father had fought in the army and navy both. Lots of fathers belonged to the East Tennessee Militia, but his father was Major Farragut; he was boss. All the fathers cleared land, built log cabins, and planted gardens. But his father built the biggest log cabin and had the best garden. And his father owned the ferryboat that crossed the Holston River; he had built the boat too.

Just like all the other fathers, only braver and

smarter and more fun. That was what Glasgow thought—until the woman whispered.

The day was just like any day—at first. Father was mending the cabin; William was kneading clay and moss into balls for Father to stuff the chinks between the logs.

"Can't I do it too?" Glasgow asked.

William snorted. "You're too little." William was four years older, and he never let Glasgow forget it. "It takes muscle to knead this stuff together."

From across the river the horn sounded for the ferry. Good! That was something he could help do! Glasgow jumped off the stump, calling, "Father! Somebody's blowing for the ferry! Can I go too?"

Father smiled and nodded. He wiped his hands on some moss, then rubbed his knuckles against Glasgow's head. "Come along!"

Glasgow ran beside him with a hop, skip, and a jump to keep up. "Can I be lookout?"

"Fine!"

Mother called from the doorway of the cabin. "Glasgow?"

"Not now!" he begged. "I've got to help Father run the ferry!"

"I'm not stopping you." She held out a little bucket. "I want you to take this mess of kraut over to Mrs. Haden. She's right by the ferry. Father will wait for you."

"Yes, ma'am." He darted back, grabbed the bucket, and ran to catch up with Father.

"And Glasgow," she called.

"Yes, ma'am?"

"Mind your manners."

"Yes, ma'am." He grabbed Father's hand. "Come on!" he begged.

But Father stood a moment, looking down at him. "Glasgow, what do I tell you about an officer and a gentleman?"

"He is kind to women and children."

"So. You must not forget."

When they reached the other side of the river, Glasgow picked up the bucket and ran up the path to Mrs. Haden's cabin. He minded his manners. Even though the door was open, he knocked and said, "Howdy, ma'am."

Mrs. Haden had a visitor. She said the lady was her cousin from Kentucky.

When Glasgow started out of the cabin he minded his manners again. "Good day, ma'am." He said it to the cousin too.

Outside the door Mrs. Haden's big black cat rubbed against his leg and purred. He stopped to pet her.

He heard the cousin ask, "Who's the little fellow?"

Then Mrs. Haden whispered, a loud, hissing whisper, like she was telling something awful.

3

"He's the son of the foreigner!"

"You mean the man that—"

"Yes!" Mrs. Haden went on talking in that awful whisper. He could not hear what she was saying— just the *hiss, hiss* of the whisper.

He clenched his fists. It wasn't so! There was nothing wrong with his father. He was the bravest man in Tennessee! In the whole world! He wished he could run back into the cabin and hit her. He'd like to hit her and yell, "Don't whisper about my father!" That's what he'd like to do—hit her and yell. But he couldn't on account of officers and gentlemen.

When they got back to their landing, Glasgow ran to the cabin ahead of Father. He wished Mother had been alone, but everybody was there. Little Nancy was rocking the baby George in his cradle; William was stacking firewood on the hearth; Mother was knitting.

"Mother," he asked, "what's a foreigner?"

Mother stopped knitting. For a moment she sat very still. Then she began knitting again. "Now where did you hear that word?"

"Mrs. Haden said it." He was so mad his voice shook. "She *whispered* it. What's a foreigner?"

Just then Father came in. "I am! I'm the for-eigner!" He sounded mad. He looked mad too.

Mother said, "Mrs. Haden just said that because

she's never been anywhere, the poor dear. I don't suppose she's ever been farther from here than you could throw a cow by the tail."

Glasgow started to laugh. But Father muttered something and stamped out of the house. William glared at Glasgow and went out too.

Mother went on talking, a little louder now, as though she wanted Father to hear. "You remember what I told you about General Lafayette? How he came from clear across the ocean to help us fight? That's what your father did too. He was a hero, just like General Lafayette."

Was Father listening? No, he was splitting firewood. Even the axe sounded mad.

"Foreigners," Mother said, "are just newcomers to a country. The Indians are the only people in America who aren't foreigners. My people were foreigners; Mrs. Haden's people were foreigners. Silly, isn't it, to look down your nose at somebody just because he didn't come from the same country that your people did?"

"Will I always be the son of a foreigner?"

"Yes. But someday that won't matter. You'll grow up to be a great man. Then people won't say your father is a foreigner. They'll say, 'That's Glasgow Farragut's father.' And Father will be so proud he'll bust the buttons off his coat!"

"He will?"

5

"Just wait and see!"

Father came back in. "Well, did you find out what a foreigner is?"

"Yes, sir! Just like General Lafayette!"

Father went over to Mother's chair and stood looking down at her. "You married a great fellow, didn't you? I suppose all your friends said, 'Poor girl, she married a foreigner!' "

Mother smiled. "What if we went across the ocean to the Island of Minorca—where you were born? Where everybody speaks Spanish. What would your people say? I can just hear them now. 'Poor man, he married a foreigner!' "

Father laughed, bent, and kissed the top of her head. "I don't know what I'd do without you."

"You'll not have to worry about that," she said. "I intend to stay around for quite a while!"

The next day Father got a letter. Suddenly the cabin was full of his laughter and shouting. "The navy! I'm going back in the navy!" He tossed the letter in Mother's lap, swung the baby high over his head, slapped William on the back, and tousled Glasgow's hair.

Mother stared at the letter. "The Naval Station at New Orleans? Isn't that awfully far away?"

"More than a thousand miles from here. Way down the Mississippi, almost to the ocean."

"How soon will we have to go?"

"I'll leave as soon as I can," he said. "Ride horseback to Natchez and take a boat from there. It'll be quicker. But you and the children won't come until fall."

"Can't we go with you?"

"No, no, dear. I don't want you in New Orleans in the summer. It's yellow-fever time. Hard on strangers. Let's see, you'll need a good big flatboat for the trip. I'll start it and have some men finish it." He sat at the table and began to draw lines on paper.

"But how can we manage the flatboat without you?"

"I'll have young Brady bring you down. He's made the trip before." He chuckled. "A good thing! That Mississippi River—he is a devil!" He whistled as he worked, then stopped and looked up, his eyes shining. "Back in the navy! And maybe our boys will get a chance to be midshipmen! And grow up to be officers in the navy!"

"Would that make you proud?" Glasgow asked.

"Prouder than anything in the world!"

"Proud enough to bust the buttons off your coat?"

Father grinned. "I can hear them now. *Pop, pop, pop!*"

"How does a boy get to be a midshipman?"

7

Father stopped smiling. "It's not easy now. The government's cut the navy down to nothing, the fools!"

"How could a boy get in?"

"Somebody important would have to speak up for you. Somebody mighty important."

"And before that," William said, "you'd have to grow a little. They don't take children in the navy."

"Don't call me a children!" Glasgow dashed at William, butted him in the stomach, and began to pound him.

"Boys!" Father didn't sound that stern very often.

Glasgow stopped. "Yes, sir?"

"Go outside and cool off."

"Yes, sir." Glasgow marched out, sat with a thud on a stump, and glowered. But soon he began to grin.

New Orleans! A naval station! Ships! Someday he'd be in the navy! A captain! And Father would be so proud he'd bust the buttons off his coat!

2. ALL ABOARD FOR
NEW ORLEANS!

Two weeks later the flatboat was started, and Father was ready to leave for New Orleans. He kissed Mother and the little ones, shook hands with Brady and the boys, mounted his horse, and started off.

The men working on the boat waved and cheered. But when Father had gone they shook their heads and began to mutter: "I'd hate to leave my family to make that trip by flatboat!"

Brady laughed. "I've made it three times and never lost a boat yet!"

"Always a first time."

"Man can get stuck on a sandbar and be stranded till a boat comes along to drag him off," one said.

9

Another nodded. "Yes, sirree. That Mississippi sure is a devil!"

At last the flatboat was done, and the workmen went away. Good! Glasgow thought. Nobody now to mumble and mutter about the river! Just Brady was with them now, and he wasn't scared.

But Glasgow found he could not forget the things the men had said. Sometimes he had nightmares about getting stuck on a sandbar and starving to death right in the middle of the river.

Early in August, Brady began to load the flatboat. Behind the flat-roofed house in the middle of the boat he piled boxes and barrels and covered them with a tarpaulin. Behind them he fixed pens for the cow and some chickens.

The last morning he carried some furniture from the cabin into the house on the boat.

Neighbors came to see them off. The men stood around looking glum. The women sniffed and wiped their eyes on the corners of their aprons. Nobody said very much—nobody but Mrs. Haden.

She talked in that awful whisper. "Poor Mrs. Farragut! It's all right for *him*—but she'll be a poor lorn creature down there with all them foreigners!"

Glasgow shot a quick glance at Mother. Had she heard Mrs. Haden? He hoped not. He clenched his fists and wished again he could yell at Mrs. Haden and hit her. Sometimes he got tired of remembering about officers and gentlemen.

"All aboard!" Brady yelled. "All aboard for New Orleans!"

Glasgow took little Nancy's hand, Mother carried the baby, and William helped Brady cast off. Men with poles shoved the boat away from the landing. They began to move.

Brady went to the back of the boat and took hold of a long oar—the longest oar Glasgow had ever seen.

"Can you row us all the way to New Orleans with that oar?"

Brady grinned. "Don't have to row. We'll be going downriver all the way. This oar is a sweep. I steer the boat with it."

"How do you come back upriver?"

"Don't worry about that. This boat isn't coming back."

Not coming back! Glasgow's stomach felt funny. He turned to Mother. "Aren't we ever coming home again?"

"Anywhere we are all together is home. Right now this boat is home. And do you know what we're going to do?"

"Help Brady?" he asked.

"Do you remember what happened July the fifth?"

11

"My birthday! Now I'm going-on-seven!"

"And it's time to begin your lessons."

"But I don't want lessons! I don't need lessons! I'm going to be a navy man!"

Brady called from the back of the boat. "Mrs. Farragut, could Glasgow help me just a minute?"

"Go along, Glasgow."

Good! No lessons!

Brady gave him a little notebook and pencil. "A captain always keeps a log. That's the record of his voyage. Will you keep the log of our voyage?"

"Yes, sir! Where do you want me to keep it?"

William meandered over, grinning.

"Just write down what I say," Brady said. "Monday, August 10, 1807. Got under way with—" He stopped. "Why aren't you writing it, Glasgow?"

William laughed. "Because he can't write." He held out his hand for the notebook. "I'll keep the log for you."

Glasgow slammed the notebook and pencil on the deck and stamped back to his mother. "All right! I'll do my lessons!"

"Glasgow?"

"Yes, ma'am."

"Look at me." He did. Finally he had to smile. "That's better."

"But I'd rather help Brady," he muttered.

When lessons were done, Brady said both boys

12

could help him. They could take turns standing forward, on the lookout for trouble. They'd need lookouts, he said, especially when they got to the Mississippi.

Glasgow remembered. "Yes, sir! That Mississippi River, he is a devil!"

"Glasgow!" Mother gasped. "Do you want your mouth washed out with soap?"

"He's just repeating what he's heard, ma'am," Brady said. "And it's not really swearing, ma'am. It's just stating the facts. Wait till we get to the Mississippi, and you'll see."

Presently they were in the muddy swift-flowing Mississippi. Brady had to watch every minute as he followed the twists and turns, keeping a lookout for any swirl of water that signaled a hidden danger. In spite of all his care, they went aground on sandbars time and again.

One day they went aground three times. The third time, a big keel boat came along, full of men laughing and singing. The men dragged the flatboat off.

Mother thanked them.

"It's nothing!" one yelled cheerfully. "Anybody helps anybody on the Mississippi! This river—he is a devil!"

Weeks passed. Then one afternoon Brady yelled, "New Orleans! Dead ahead!"

Glasgow dashed forward to stare at all the big

13

ships and the tall masts. If only he could be a mid-shipman right away! Climbing up the tallest mast on the biggest ship!

Presently they were tied up at a wharf and Father was there, laughing, shouting, hugging everybody. Then he said, "Excuse me! I'm too happy! I forget!" He turned to the navy man with him. "This is Captain David Porter."

The captain had a ruddy face, twinkling black eyes, and curly gray hair. He shook hands with everybody. "And you're Glasgow, eh? I hear you want to join the navy."

"Yes, sir. But Father says it's not easy now. That somebody mighty important would have to speak up for me." He eyed the captain's epaulettes. "You're pretty important. Maybe you could speak up for me? Today? Or maybe tomorrow?"

"You're a little young for it now, lad. But in a few years—when you're eleven or twelve—I'll speak up for you."

Mother stared. "They don't take boys to be mid-shipmen that young, do they? When do they go to school?"

"Right on shipboard, ma'am. The chaplain doubles as teacher. Preaches on Sunday and teaches weekdays."

Father said, "And the ship's officers teach the boys the really important things."

15

The captain nodded. "Every minute a middy is on deck he's learning. Every time the O.D.—the officer of the deck—shouts an order every middy on deck shouts it after him. Like this, Glasgow. Shout this after me: 'Lay aloft topmen!' "

"Lay aloft topmen!"

"That's it! You hear it, you say it, and then you watch what happens. That's how you learn."

Glasgow looked toward the big ships in the river. "Which ship is yours, sir? The biggest one?"

The captain scowled. "None of them. The navy doesn't have a proper ship on this station. Nothing but shallow-draft gunboats to patrol the water around here. A fine business!"

"But we'll live near the big ships, won't we?" Glasgow asked. "And I'll get to go on them?"

Father shook his head. "It's too hard to find a house in New Orleans. Some of us navy men have settled along Lake Pontchartrain. Just a few miles from here."

The next summer Glasgow stood scowling across the waters of Lake Pontchartrain. Miles away from New Orleans! Nothing to do but say his lessons and help look after the little ones. Mother was busy taking care of the house and the new little baby, Elizabeth. Busy—but never too busy to hear him say his lessons.

How long before he could be in the navy? William was already a midshipman, with a blue coat and shiny buttons. But William was four years older. Four whole years! Would he have to wait that long before Captain Porter would speak up for him?

One sweltering day that summer Father came running from the lake, yelling, "Elizabeth! Get a bed ready!"

Two men followed, carrying Captain Porter.

"What happened?" Glasgow whispered.

"Sunstroke," Father said. "He'd been fishing. We found him in the bottom of a rowboat."

"He'll get well, won't he?"

"We hope so."

"I'll help take care of him," Glasgow said. "He is my good friend."

"You can help, dear," Mother told him. "Keep Nancy and little George outside so it will be quiet for the captain."

Three days later, when Glasgow was playing with Nancy and George, their neighbor Mrs. Wilson came out in the yard. She had the baby in one arm and was carrying a bundle of clothes in the other.

"You and the little ones are coming home with me, Glasgow."

"Where's Mother?"

17

"She doesn't feel good."

"Who's taking care of the captain?"

"Mrs. Hodges right now. Tonight someone else will spell her. Come along, dear."

"Yes, ma'am." He gave one hand to Nancy and one to George and followed her.

A whole week passed. Sometimes women came, stood out in the yard, and talked to Mrs. Wilson. They whispered.

One afternoon Mrs. Wilson beckoned him out into the yard. "Glasgow, you're going to have to help your father."

"Take care of the captain?" Then he read it in her eyes. "The captain died?"

"Yes. You'll have to help your poor father. Cheer him up."

"Mother will do that. I remember once—" He stopped.

Mrs. Wilson was crying. "Oh, Glasgow! Your poor mother! It was the yellow fever."

"*No!*"

"We'll take care of the little ones, dear. But your father needs you."

"Yes, ma'am." Dazed, he went into the house, made a bundle of his clothes, and went home.

3. OFF SOUNDINGS

Father was sitting on a stump in the yard, staring at the ground. He didn't look like Father. He looked like an old man.

"Father?"

"Eh? Oh, it's you, lad." He put an arm around Glasgow. Then he stared at the ground again.

What could he do to cheer Father up? He noticed Father's trim little yawl in the lake. "I wish we could go for a sail."

"Eh? Yes, yes, come along."

After a while the wind rose and the waves kicked up until the lake looked almost like an ocean. Father's face came alive as he fought to handle the boat in the wind. Then it began to get dark.

Father sighed. "I guess we'd better go back."

19

In front of their house, Father looked like an old man again. "I can't go on living here!" he muttered.

Maybe, Glasgow thought, we'll go to New Orleans—where all the ships are!

But the next summer Glasgow was farther than ever from New Orleans—a hundred miles away. Father had bought a plantation on the Pascagoula River. He went back and forth to New Orleans in his yawl. He wasn't home very much. A Mr. Meeker bossed the plantation. Mrs. Meeker ran the house and took care of the children. There were only three of them at home now. William was in the navy; the baby was with a Mrs. Dupont on another plantation.

A hundred miles from New Orleans! Glasgow sat on their landing with six-year-old Nancy and four-year-old George, wondering again if he'd ever have a chance now to get in the navy.

Mrs. Meeker came out and picked up little George. "No use looking for your father today. It's coming up a blow."

Just then Nancy yelled, "There he comes!" And they saw Father's yawl, heeling over in the wind, cutting through the water, and the spray flying.

"That man!" Mrs. Meeker said. "He's not afraid of the Old Nick himself!"

Father came alongside the landing. "Ahoy the

20

house! You two want to go for a sail?"

Mrs. Meeker gasped. "Mr. Farragut! It's no time to take those children out! You'll scare them to death!"

Father laughed. "Bah! Now's the time to get over being afraid."

Soon Nancy and Glasgow were in the boat, hanging on for dear life and squinching their eyes against the spray.

Father's eyes were shining. "Fun, isn't it?" he shouted.

Nancy giggled. "Fun!" she yelled.

Glasgow swallowed hard. Then he laughed too. "Fun!" he yelled. If a girl thought it was fun, he couldn't be scared!

The wind blew harder and the water got rougher. "Guess we'd better go back," Father said, "or Mrs. Meeker will have a fit!"

Back at their landing he helped them out, made the boat snug, then, head bowed, went toward the house.

Nancy clutched Glasgow's hand. "Whew! I was scared to death!"

"Scared? But you laughed!"

"Of course. You were brave. I had to be brave too—outside. But inside—" She touched her stomach. "Inside, I was scared."

The next day another sailboat came to their

landing. A young man in uniform called, "Ahoy the house!" He had snapping black eyes, a ruddy face, and curly black hair.

Father hurried out to meet him. "This is Commander David Porter," he said. "He's in charge of the station at New Orleans now."

"You're Captain Porter's son," Glasgow said. "You look like him, sir. He was my good friend."

"You were all certainly good friends of my father," Mr. Porter said.

"Anybody would have done what we did," Father told him. "Everybody liked the captain."

"Thank you. Mr. Farragut, my wife and I have been talking—about how we'd like to repay you for your kindness. We'd like to take one of your boys to live with us. We'd try to give him a good home. When he's old enough—if he wants it—I'd see that he gets an appointment as a midshipman."

"I'll go!" Glasgow did not realize he had spoken until he heard Nancy gasp. She clapped her hands over her mouth and stared at him, big-eyed.

Father stood looking out over the water. "It would be a fine chance for him." His voice sounded tired. "You can do more for him than I can. If it's what he wants, he can go."

"Good enough. If you can put me up for the night, we'll start in the morning. Can you be ready, Glasgow?"

Glasgow saluted. "Aye, aye, sir!"

Nancy said she had forgotten something and ran into the house. She didn't come to the supper table. She said she wasn't hungry.

That night Glasgow had a hard time trying to go to sleep. For a long time he heard the rumble of voices out on the porch. Then Mr. Porter said good-night, and the house was still. Glasgow slid out of bed and went out on the porch. Father was alone, sitting the way he did most of the time, his head bowed, staring at nothing.

Glasgow sat down by him. "You're not feeling bad, are you?"

"No, no. It's a fine chance for you."

"It's because I want you to bust your buttons."

"Eh?" Then Father remembered. He chuckled and hugged Glasgow. "You'll make me proud all right, lad. I know you will. Remember, a long time ago, when I told you about an officer and a gentleman?"

"Yes, sir. He is kind to women and children."

"Yes. That was enough for a little boy to understand. But now I can tell you more." He straightened and his voice was deep. "An officer and a gentleman is faithful to the men over him and fair to the men under him. He lives for his country. If the time comes, he dies for her. Will you remember that I said that?"

"Yes, sir! Always! And I will make you proud.

23

I'll work hard! I'll—" He stopped. He was afraid his voice would shake.

Saying good-bye the next morning was hard. Nancy was fighting tears. Father's mouth was smiling, but his eyes weren't. Only little George was cheerful. A four-year-old doesn't know much.

Soon Glasgow was in the boat with Mr. Porter, trying to swallow the lump in his throat.

After a while Mr. Porter said, "How'd you like to take the tiller?"

"Aye, aye, sir!" The lump in his throat went away. By the time they got to New Orleans he felt fine. He was all over being a baby. He marched along, head up, chin in.

Presently Mr. Porter said, "Here we are!"

Mrs. Porter was a pretty young woman with blue eyes and curly brown hair. She held out her arms to him. Suddenly all the months that he had missed his mother hit him. He ducked his head against her and fought tears.

She didn't seem to notice. "You'll find your room at the head of the stairs. First door to the right. Or should I say 'to starboard'?"

"Yes, ma'am. Thank you, ma'am." He bolted up the stairs. Through a blur of tears he saw a bed with a patchwork quilt, a washstand with a bowl and pitcher, a little desk. He sat at the desk with his head on his arms. Finally he straightened, sniffed angrily, and said, "Baby!" He washed his face in cold water.

Mr. Porter called, "Glasgow! Supper at five bells! Know what time that is?"

Glasgow counted up on his fingers. "Aye, aye, sir! Six thirty!" He squared his shoulders and marched down the stairs. He was through being a baby. From now on he would act like a midshipman.

The next morning after breakfast Mrs. Porter brought some books to the table. "How much have you been to school, Glasgow?"

"Not any, ma'am. Mother taught me until . . . But I haven't had anybody to teach me since."

"I see." She opened a book. "Try reading in this." He tried, but he stumbled over a lot of words.

She gave him a slate and pencil. "Try writing words you remember." When he stopped, she smiled at the list. "You certainly like ships, don't you?"

"Yes, ma'am."

She tried him on arithmetic. She was very patient. She never frowned or looked surprised at what he didn't know. But he had a feeling he must be quite a disappointment.

When Mr. Porter came to dinner, he said, "How did lessons go?"

25

"Not very well, sir. I don't know very much."

"Just work hard, and you'll get along all right," Mr. Porter said. "How'd you like to go to the office with me this afternoon?"

"Office!"

"Did you think I spent all my time on shipboard? Lad, the commandant of a Naval Station is lashed to his desk two-thirds of the time."

The office that afternoon was dull. Mr. Porter sat reading papers and talking. A young man he called a secretary wrote down what he said in funny writing, then wrote it out again in regular writing. Two other secretaries were making copies of letters.

At last Mr. Porter said, "Well, that's it for today." Outside the office he asked, "How do you like my job?"

"It's awful! I—I—mean—"

"You meant just what you said. And I agree with you. After this assignment if they give me another desk job, I'll resign from the navy! I swear I will!"

"Sir!"

Then Mr. Porter smiled. "Don't worry, lad. I'll growl a lot, but I'll never resign from the navy. Never!"

"Thank you, sir."

"You'll get to be a midshipman, all right. Just pitch in and study hard."

"Yes, sir."

The next morning he tried to do better, but he knew he was doing worse. Time and again he had to say, "I don't know, ma'am." Finally the words wouldn't come. He could only shake his head.

Mrs. Porter stopped and smiled. "Glasgow, don't worry so about it! When you don't know, just say you don't know. Then I'll help you find out."

"Yes, ma'am."

"No more worrying?"

"No, ma'am."

And he didn't worry again until the next spring. Then the Porters had a little baby boy. They named him William.

Glasgow tried three times before he managed to ask Mrs. Porter, "Do you still want me? When you have a boy of your own?"

"Glasgow, of course we do! Babies are sweet, but you are lots more fun. Our home will always be your home. Will you remember that?"

"Yes, ma'am. Thank you, ma'am."

New orders came for Mr. Porter. In June he would sail to Washington, D.C., for duty at the Navy Yard. "Another desk job!" he growled. "I'll resign! I swear I will!"

Mrs. Porter only smiled and winked at Glasgow.

The day they were to sail, Father, Nancy, and little George were there to say good-bye. Even

27

William got to come and see them off. Nancy stood blinking her eyes and biting her lips. Glasgow didn't try to talk. He just saluted.

But once on the ship he felt better. At last—on a real ship! The bomb brig *Vesuvius* wasn't very big, but she was a proper ship.

And he knew what he was going to do. He'd listen to every order the O.D. gave and whisper it after him.

"One hundred miles down the Mississippi," Mr. Porter said, "then salt water! Off soundings! That's the life!"

And finally they were out in the Gulf of Mexico. Glasgow stood with his feet spread, feeling the motion of the deck. Yes, this was the life!

An hour later he huddled in his bunk. *Seasick!* And nobody else was! Even little William was laughing and crowing. *Seasick!* He wished he could die.

4. "THREE POUNDS OF UNIFORM . . ."

After three days Glasgow had his sea legs. He spent all the time—when he wasn't having lessons —on deck. He listened to every order the O.D. gave and whispered it after him. Someday he'd shout those orders right out. He stood down on the shelf they called the chains, with the water foaming past, while a sailor threw a hand lead in the water to check the depth. He scampered up the ratlines like a monkey, perched high on the main mast, and stared over the ocean.

On the Fourth of July the crew fired salutes morning, noon, and night. Tomorrow he would be going-on-ten. How much longer before he could be a midshipman?

The next morning Mrs. Porter surprised him

with a new shirt she had made by hand, and a letter that Nancy had printed:

HAPPY BIRTHDAY, GLASGOW. I AM THINKING OF YOU. I HOPE YOU COME BACK SOON. I LOVE YOU. NANCY

He scrambled up the ratlines to a high perch. The wind was his good friend. It dried tears before they ran down. What was the matter with him? Why didn't he grow up? What made him get so homesick? He watched the white waves foaming behind the ship. Someday he'd be on his own ship. Someday . . .

What was Washington going to be like? Mr. Porter had groaned about it. "Another desk job! I'll resign! I swear I will!"

Mrs. Porter only smiled at that.

Washington was fine. Glasgow went with Mr. Porter to the Navy Yard, saw ships a-building, and listened to navy talk.

One morning Mr. Porter came to his room. "Dress in your best this morning. We're going to see somebody mighty important."

Glasgow almost asked who. But that was not the way a navy man answered. He said, "Aye, aye, sir."

Two hours later he stood before the Secretary of the Navy, Mr. Paul Hamilton.

"So," Mr. Hamilton said, "this little fellow wants

to be a midshipman, does he?"

Little fellow! Glasgow fought to keep from scowling. There was only one thing worse than having someone call you "little fellow." That was to have a grown-up talk over your head as if you weren't there or couldn't speak for yourself.

He stood as tall as he could. "Yes, sir. I want to be a midshipman, sir."

Mr. Hamilton asked, "And how old is this little fellow?"

Glasgow clenched his teeth, then said, "I'm almost going-on-eleven, sir."

Mr. Hamilton finally looked at him. "And just what does that mean?"

"On my tenth birthday I'll be going-on-eleven, sir."

Mr. Hamilton's eyebrows went up. "So you're not ten yet. You're only nine?"

"Yes, sir."

"And when were you nine?"

Glasgow could feel his ears getting red. "July the fifth, sir."

Mr. Hamilton chuckled and talked over Glasgow's head again. "So he hasn't been nine very long, has he? I tell you what, Commander. When the little fellow is ten—if I've heard good reports of him—he shall be a midshipman." He finally looked down at Glasgow again. "Mr. Farragut, midshipman. How does that sound?"

Almost a whole year to wait. But Glasgow mustered a smile. "Thank you, sir." At least he'd be in Washington. He'd get to visit the Navy Yard. He'd learn more about ships. He'd—

"Is your family staying in Washington, Commander?"

Mr. Porter shook his head. Washington in the summer, he said, was no fit place for man or beast. Mrs. Porter and the children would go to Green Bank, their home in Chester, Pennsylvania.

Mr. Hamilton nodded. A beautiful place. He was sure the little fellow would enjoy it. And he would like going to school in Chester.

School!

Glasgow had been in school only two weeks when he brought a note home to Mrs. Porter. She read it, then handed it to him to read. Glasgow, the note said, was a bright boy and well-behaved, but he did not seem to pay attention.

"What's the trouble?" she asked quietly.

"I'm sorry, ma'am. I try. But I—I just get to thinking."

"What about?"

"Ships."

"Oh, Glasgow!" She sounded so loving and so sad.

"I'll try harder, ma'am! Honest!"

32

And he did try harder. By November he had brought home only four more notes. But during the first ten days of December he brought home three more.

"Glasgow," Mrs. Porter said, "I don't know what to do about you!"

The fourteenth of December he walked to the door of Green Bank with his feet dragging. Another note. Why, oh why, couldn't he keep his mind on his lessons?

He fooled around as long as he could, hanging up his wraps. At last he couldn't stall any longer. He marched to the library with the note, then stopped short in the doorway. "Mr. Porter! Sir!" He didn't know if he dared smile. Had Mr. Porter heard about the notes?

Mr. Porter beamed and held out both hands. "You're looking fine. Have you been taking good care of the family?"

"Yes, sir." At least that was the truth. But he knew he had to tell the rest of it. He straightened. "But, sir, I haven't done very well in school. I—I can't seem to keep my mind on it."

"I see." Mr. Porter stopped smiling. "Well, at least you had the decency to tell me about it."

Glasgow looked quickly at Mrs. Porter.

She shook her head. "No, Glasgow. I haven't said anything about the notes. I knew you'd do that yourself."

"Yes, ma'am. Thank you, ma'am. Here's another one." He handed over the note. "Uh—uh—excuse me, ma'am. I think I'll study a while before supper." He ran upstairs to his room.

He tried to study, but he could not. What if Mr. Porter wrote to the Secretary of the Navy and told him Glasgow was a poor student? Then Mr. Hamilton might write a letter that said:

> *Dear Glasgow Farragut,*
>
> *I hear you are not much of a student. I am afraid you are not the stuff of which officers are made. Therefore . . .*

For the next few days he fought desperately to keep his mind on his lessons. But it was no use. On December 19, he carried another note home.

As he entered the library he had a feeling the Porters had stopped talking in the middle of a word.

Mr. Porter held out a letter. "For you, Glasgow."

From Washington. It had happened.

"Aren't you going to open it?" Mr. Porter asked.

"Yes, sir." He sat down because his knees were shaking. His fingers were shaking too. He had a hard time breaking the seal and unfolding the stiff paper. His name jumped at him:

> *. . . KNOW YE, That reposing special Trust*
> *and Confidence in the Patriotism, Valour,*
> *Fidelity, and Abilities of*
> *GLASGOW FARRAGUT*
> *I do appoint him a Midshipman in the*
> NAVY OF THE UNITED STATES. *. . .*

There was more, but the words were blurring.

Mr. Porter said, "Go wash up a bit, Glasgow. We'll have to go see Mr. Eyre, the Justice of the Peace. You'll have to take your oath before him."

"Aye, aye, sir!"

In Mr. Eyre's office Glasgow's heart was hammering so hard that Mr. Eyre's voice sounded far away, but his own voice was steady as he repeated the oath:

> I, Glasgow Farragut, appointed Midshipman in the Navy of the United States, do solemnly swear to bear true allegiance to the United States of America and to serve them honestly and faithfully against all their enemies and opposers . . .

On the way home he felt as though his grin was wrapped around his ears. Mr. Farragut, midshipman! Not quite nine and a half and already in the navy. Soon he'd be on a ship. Mr. Farragut, midshipman, reporting to his ship! "Will I report to my ship before Christmas or right after?"

"You'll wait for orders," Mr. Porter said. "That's what a navy man always does. He gets ready. Then he waits for orders."

"Oh . . ."

"You see, the navy always has to be ready for anything. So men have to be standing by, ready to go where they're needed. Right now, there are midshipmen, lieutenants, commanders, and captains all waiting for orders. They don't know when those orders will come or where those orders will send them. It all depends on what the navy needs right then."

"Then I'm just—"

"You are Mr. Farragut, midshipman awaiting orders. Till those orders come, you'll stay in school and learn all you can."

"Yes, sir. I see, sir."

So it wasn't going to be any different. Not for a while.

Home again, Mr. Porter said, "Here is something to help you remember this day."

"Thank you, sir!" He opened the watch and read the engraving:

From D.P. to D.G.F., U.S.N., 1810

To D.G.F.—but his initials weren't D.G.F. His

36

name was James Glasgow Farragut. Nobody had ever called him James. It ought to be *To J.G.F.* Mr. Porter had made a mistake. He'd feel awful if he knew. D.G.F. That could stand for David Glasgow Farragut. I like that, Glasgow said to himself. After all, he had never known the man he was named for. And he did know somebody named David! That was Captain Porter's name! Yes, from here on his name would be David Glasgow Farragut.

"And here's something else." Mr. Porter handed him a fat book—*The Practical Navigator* by Nathaniel Bowditch. "When you know everything in there, you can take a ship anywhere in the world."

"Thank you, sir!"

There were whole pages of tiny figures; there was lots of mathematics he couldn't understand. But one part of the book was called "Sea Terms." Now that made sense. Mr. Farragut, midshipman, would learn every word of that part!

In August of 1811—Glasgow had been ten just a month—he stood in a tailor's shop in Norfolk, Virginia, putting on a uniform.

The tailor peered over his glasses and grinned. "Smallest uniform I ever made. Can't figure what Captain Porter's thinking about, taking you to sea."

Glasgow didn't bother to answer. Tomorrow he

would be done with landlubbers. He would report to his ship, the *Essex*. Captain Porter was out of town, but he had told Glasgow exactly what to do and had given him a letter to deliver to Lieutenant Downes, executive officer on the *Essex*.

That night Glasgow packed, unpacked, and re-packed four times. He was so afraid he would oversleep and miss the boat at nine thirty that he was up at six o'clock. At two bells—nine o'clock—he was already on the wharf. After five minutes he would have given anything to have been some-where else. Anywhere. A gang of roustabouts eyed him, nudged each other, and whispered behind their hands.

The ringleader seemed to be the one they called Fatso. His little pig eyes studied Glasgow up and down. A loose-lipped grin, a wink at the others, and he said in a piping falsetto, "Maaa-maaa! Where are you? I'm afraid of the dark!"

The others slapped their legs and whooped.

Fatso thought up more things to say. More whoops of laughter.

Glasgow clenched his teeth and turned his back on them. He stared across the water toward the *Essex*, riding at anchor. Soon he'd be there. He'd never, never have to listen to these roustabouts again.

Finally he saw a boat put out from the *Essex*. A

tall midshipman stood in the stern sheets. A crew of husky sailors manned the oars. When the boat glided in by the wharf, the roustabouts stopped talking.

Glasgow smiled and saluted the tall midshipman. "Mr. Farragut, sir, reporting to the *Essex*."

The tall midshipman had red hair, freckles, and a friendly grin. "Hullo there, Farragut. I'm Matthews. Nothing else from Captain Porter this morning, eh?" He spoke to the biggest sailor. "Stow Mr. Farragut's gear, Hawley, and we'll push off."

"Aye, aye, sir!" The big fellow lifted down the bag as though it didn't weigh a pound.

Matthews gave his orders. "Aye, aye, sir!" The oars rose and fell as one as they pulled for the *Essex*.

What an air of command Matthews had! How important he looked standing there in the stern sheets. How long, Glasgow wondered, before he'd be able to command a boat that way?

The roustabouts watched silently as the boat pulled away. Glasgow was glad of that. He would not have wanted Matthews and the sailors to hear what they had been saying. Thank heavens, he was done with all that! He could forget about them. He was reporting to the *Essex*!

He'd be all right when he got to his ship. Mr.

Downes was going to be surprised at how much he knew—that downstairs was below, and upstairs was topside, and into the rigging was aloft. That to the front was forward, and to the back was aft. That . . .

But as they drew near the *Essex* he gulped and his heart hammered. How huge she was towering up out of the water over them.

He managed to reach the deck without stumbling. He remembered to salute the quarter-deck. He remembered to salute the O.D.

"Mr. Farragut reporting, sir. I have a letter for Lieutenant Downes, sir."

The O.D. blinked as he looked at Glasgow, but he didn't smile. "Matthews, suppose you take Farragut to the First."

"Aye, aye, sir." Matthews led the way below to the gun deck and below that to the berth deck. He walked aft to a wall that reached from starboard to port across the deck and knocked on the door of the wardroom.

"Come!"

Several officers sat around a table reading or talking. They looked Glasgow up and down too. But nobody laughed.

No more roustabouts! Cheerfully, almost smiling, Glasgow saluted. "Mr. Farragut reporting, sir."

Mr. Downes took the captain's letter, read it, rubbed his chin, and studied Glasgow. "Orders for you, Farragut."

"Aye, aye, sir!"

"Every morning at three bells you will have command of the captain's boat. You will take it to the wharf where Matthews picked you up this morning. You will wait there for any message from Captain Porter. It will be your responsibility to keep order on the boat, to see that your men do not leave the boat. Even if you have to wait half an hour, the men will stay with the boat. You understand?"

Every morning! To wait at the wharf! Maybe for half an hour! Glasgow wished he could say, Please, not me! But in the navy there was only one answer. He wet his lips, stiffened, pulled in his chin, and said, "Aye, aye, sir."

5. ". . . AND SEVENTY POUNDS OF FIGHT"

To wait at the wharf every morning! Numbly, Glasgow saluted and followed Matthews from the wardroom. Matthews nodded toward the space just ahead where there were two tables and some chests. "The steerage," he said. "Our quarters."

A sailor had brought Glasgow's gear. Matthews showed him a chest where he could stow it and hooks overhead where he could swing his hammock. "A good thing you'll have a hammock-boy to reach up and swing it for you and to take it down in the morning, isn't it?" But his grin was friendly.

Glasgow smiled weakly back at him.

Matthews cocked his head. "Look, Farragut, you're not worrying about anything, are you?

About commanding the captain's boat? There's nothing to it. I can teach you the orders in five minutes. And the men won't give you any trouble. When an officer gives an order, there's just one answer: 'Aye, aye, sir!' Come on, I'll go over the orders with you. First . . ."

Glasgow took a deep breath to steady himself and tried to listen. But when he tried to remember, it was all a jumble.

"You *are* sweating, aren't you?" Matthews' eyes were understanding. "That's all right. I remember my first day. Come on, let's try again."

After four times, Glasgow got it right.

"See!" Matthews was cheerful. "Nothing to it. Well, we'd better report to the schoolroom."

"School!"

"Every morning for two hours. Two bells to six bells. You're lucky. Long as we're in port, you'll miss at least half of it. If the captain's late, maybe you can miss all of it sometimes!"

Glasgow shivered and followed Matthews above to the gun deck. A canvas curtain partitioned off a section on the starboard side, just forward of the captain's cabin. Six boys sat around a table, scowling and squeaking slate pencils.

A roly-poly man came outside to speak to them. "You're later than usual this morning, Matthews."

"Yes, sir. Special duty, sir. Chaplain Adams, this is Midshipman Farragut."

43

"*Humph*. How old are you?"

"Ten, sir."

"*Humph*. Where are you in algebra?"

"Algebra? Uh—I'm not anywhere, sir."

"I was afraid of that. Well, maybe we'll have time for some good solid work before we sail."

"Mr. Farragut won't have much time while we're in port, sir. He's to have charge of the captain's boat."

"*Tsch, tsch!* I don't suppose we could arrange for someone else to have that duty?"

For a moment hope jumped in Glasgow's chest.

But Matthews said gently, "Sir, it's the captain's orders."

The chaplain sighed, then said, "Well, come along. I'll give you a book, and you can start getting acquainted with algebra."

Glasgow sat at a table by Matthews, opened the book, looked at a page, batted his eyes, and looked again. *A* plus *B* equals *C*. What in the name of sense?

Matthews whispered, "Don't let him worry you. After we sail, the officers keep our school time whittled down to size. And you'll get out of at least half of it all the time we're in port."

For the first time in his life Glasgow felt that school would be better than something else. But Matthews was certainly friendly. If all the other middies were like him . . .

One of them wasn't—Channing, the oldest of the lot. He was tall and thin, with pale yellow hair, pale blue eyes, and a mouth that seemed made to curl in a sneer.

Back in the steerage after class Glasgow met the other boys.

Channing looked him up and down, slowly, deliberately. "Well, well, what have we here?"

Glasgow remembered the day he would have yelled, butted Channing in the stomach, and begun pounding. Now he mustered a grin. "The beginnings of a navy man, Channing."

Another middy laughed. "That's telling him!"

Channing shrugged and strode away.

Another boy said, "But you *are* kind of little, you know."

Then everybody laughed, and Glasgow laughed with them. This was his world. His ship where . . . He thought again of the roustabouts and shivered inside.

Bong-bong. Two bells. Nine o'clock. Almost time for him to take the captain's boat to the wharf. Already his hands were sweating, and his mouth was dry. He'd lived through a whole week of it. Three times he had seen Captain Porter striding to the wharf as they approached. Those mornings there was not a word from the roustabouts. But the other mornings when the boat had

45

had to wait—that had been awful. Every day Fatso thought up another taunt to add to all the others.

Glasgow took his place in the boat, facing his men. What big fellows they were. Especially Hawley. Hawley, he thought, could pick me up with one hand and hold me over his head.

Once more he gave them their orders. No matter what the roustabouts said, they would pay no attention. Eyes front!

As always, the men said, "Aye, aye, sir!" But they growled the words in their throats. Hawley growled deepest.

As they approached the wharf Glasgow looked hard for that short, sturdy figure in blue, marching along with that brisk, thudding stride. But he was not in sight. The roustabouts were waiting. Fatso was talking to them.

As the crew brought the boat alongside and made fast, Fatso waddled over and leaned to study Glasgow. "I wonder where they got the little feller?"

As always the others joined in.

"S'pose his mother knows he's out?"

"Wonder who tucks him in at night?"

The boat's crew sat motionless, eyes front. But their eyes were blazing, and the muscles knotted in their jaws.

46

Then Fatso's voice got louder. "You know, men, we gotta *do* something for the *Essex*. Yes, sirree! We gotta see that this little feller grows! Yes, sirree! We gotta sprinkle him so he'll grow!" He lifted a sprinkling can, upending it, and sprayed a shower of muddy water on Glasgow.

With a bellow Hawley stood, lashed out with an oar, and caught Fatso on the side of the head. Blood ran down his face. Hawley leaped onto the wharf.

With a roar the whole crew scrambled from the boat. The roustabouts took to their heels, with the sailors right behind them. Glasgow raced after them, waving his sword and yelling, "Go to it, my hearties! Go to it!"

Ten minutes later the lot of them—navy men and roustabouts—stood in the police station.

"What's all this?" the chief of police asked.

"Rowdies from the *Essex*, sir," a policeman said. "They left their boat and started a fight."

Glasgow stepped forward. "Sir!"

But the chief motioned for silence. He looked at Fatso's bleeding head. "Who did that?"

Hawley straightened. "I did, sir. The name is Hawley, sir. I did it, sir, because he insulted the American flag, sir!"

"Insulted the flag? How?"

"With a sprinkling can, sir."

"*What!*"

Again Glasgow tried to speak. "Sir, I—"

"Later, little fellow." The chief glared at Hawley. "Now tell me what in the devil you're talking about."

Hawley explained about the captain's boat and the rowdies. "We've put up with it, sir, for a week because we had our orders from Mr. Farragut. But this morning was too much! That one"—he jerked a thumb at Fatso—"that one insulted the American flag, sir! With a sprinkling can, sir!"

The chief ran his fingers through his gray thatch. "For two cents I'd give the lot of you ten days in jail."

This time Glasgow managed to make himself heard. "You can't punish my men, sir. It was my responsibility!"

"Who the devil are you?"

"Mr. Farragut, sir. In command of the captain's boat."

Just then there was a stir at the doorway behind them. Glasgow heard the thud of quick heels on the wooden floor. His men heard it too. They stiffened to attention. Nobody had to turn to know who was coming in. Glasgow's heart lurched. He snapped a salute and held it.

The chief said, "Captain Porter! Thank the Lord! Maybe you can make head or tail out of this. All I hear is that someone insulted the American flag with a sprinkling can!"

Captain Porter gave Glasgow a long, deliberate stare. When he spoke his voice was cold and flat. "At ease, Mr. Farragut."

Glasgow lowered his hand. He pressed his thumbs against his legs to try to keep his hand from shaking.

"Your crew left the boat this morning?"

"Yes, sir."

"Even though you commanded them to stay?"

Glasgow wet his lips. "But I didn't command them to stay, sir. I ran right along with them, waving my sword and yelling like the very . . . and yelling, sir."

"Why did the men leave the boat?"

"That man, sir—the one with the bloody head— he insulted the uniform of the United States Navy, sir. He sprinkled water on me to make me grow, sir."

Captain Porter wheeled, stood with his back to his men, and jerked out a handkerchief. The chief jerked out a handkerchief too. They both seemed to have quite a coughing spell.

Finally the captain said, "Take your men to the boat, Mr. Farragut. Wait for me."

"Aye, aye, sir."

As Glasgow marched his men back to the boat

words hammered through his head in time to the thudding feet: "KNOW YE, That reposing special Trust and Confidence in GLASGOW FARRAGUT ..."

He had failed. He had not lived up to the special "Trust and Confidence" of the President of the United States.

In the boat the men sat motionless, waiting. Glasgow stood motionless, waiting . . . and waiting. What would Captain Porter say to him?

At last the captain strode up. He handed two letters to Glasgow. "For Mr. Downes," he said. That was all. He marched away.

The minute they went on deck Glasgow knew that word of the fight had got there ahead of them. Then he remembered about the quartermaster and his glass. When a ship was at anchor the quartermaster kept a constant lookout for anything that moved. He would have seen the fight and passed the word.

Glasgow saluted the quarter-deck, then the O.D., and took the letters below to Mr. Downes. Had he—yes, he had heard of the fight too. His glance was cool. He took the letters. Then his nod dismissed Glasgow.

Chaplain Adams stopped talking as Glasgow entered the schoolroom. "Mr. Farragut!"

Six bells. The middies jumped up, slammed

50

books shut, grabbed slates, and bolted.

Glasgow waited for what was coming. He knew he might as well.

"Mr. Farragut! Every morning you miss half your lessons. And you are not such a good student that you can afford to miss any time. This morning you have missed it all."

"I'm sorry, sir. It was an emergency, sir."

The chaplain dismissed him with a *Humph*!

Glasgow went topside, walked forward by the starboard bulkhead, stood on a block, and stared across the water. What was going to happen to him? He had a funny feeling, like he was sick at his stomach in his chest.

Behind him a voice rumbled, "Mr. Farragut, sir." Even though the man's usual bellow was down to a rumble, Glasgow knew it was William Kingsbury, one of the bosun's mates. He turned to a huge, hawk-nosed man with his leather-brown face and shaggy gray hair.

William Kingsbury was grinning. "I got to see part of it, sir. The fight. One of the quartermasters let me have his glass. He knew I'd known your father."

"You did!"

"Served with him in the Revolution. I'll never forget that man! The nerve of him! When you took off up the street, waving your sword—I knew you was a chip off the old block, lad . . . sir."

"Thank you!" The sick feeling in his chest went away. "Thank *you*!"

An orderly approached and eyed Glasgow sternly. "Mr. Downes' compliments, sir. He'll see you below."

"Thank you." The sick feeling was back. His hands were shaking. Even his knees were shaking now. He started toward the hatch.

"*Hssst!*" the orderly whispered. "Don't worry, Farragut. I heard them talking. Mr. Downes and Mr. Finch. Talking and laughing. Laughing fit to kill. Mr. Downes read part of the captain's letter. Where the captain said you are 'three pounds of uniform and seventy pounds of fight.' They laughed fit to kill."

"Thank you!" The shakes and the sick feeling were gone. Head up, Glasgow marched to the wardroom.

Mr. Downes was alone. He was not laughing. He was not even smiling. "Farragut, you realize the captain could not reprimand an officer in front of his men?"

"Yes, sir."

"But you know you deserve a reprimand?"

"Yes, sir."

"You failed in your responsibility."

"Yes, sir."

52

"Since you failed, you are relieved of that responsibility. The rest of the time we are in port another midshipman will command the captain's boat."

"Aye, aye, sir."

"That's all."

Glasgow wished he could go topside again, but the boys in the steerage had seen him go into the wardroom. They were waiting for him to come out. He went forward. He was still trying to puzzle the whole thing out. *Three pounds of uniform and seventy pounds of fight.* That didn't sound like the captain was mad. And Mr. Downes and Mr. Finch had laughed.

It was very quiet in the steerage. There was a chilly feeling in the air. Were the boys blaming him? Ashamed of him because he hadn't measured up to the "Trust and Confidence" of the President of the United States?

Even Matthews was looking at him thoughtfully. "Please God, don't let Matthews be ashamed of me!" he prayed.

Channing confronted him, lip curled. "Well, Farragut! What happened? What did the First say? Of course, no matter what he thought, he'd have to follow the captain's orders. How about it, Farragut? What did the captain order him to do?"

53

Glasgow's anger boiled up and steadied him. He even smiled when he shrugged. "I'm demoted. Someone else will command the captain's boat."

Matthews' laugh boomed out. "Yah, Channing! I told you he'd catch it!" He grinned at Glasgow. "Channing was so sure you were the captain's pet—that he wouldn't punish you. Well, Channing?"

Before Channing could make an answer a summons came. Channing would report to the wardroom. He swaggered aft.

The other boys grinned at Glasgow. And something dawned on him. *No matter what the captain thought, he had to punish me!*

Matthews said, "Poor boy. Two hours of school every morning. Come on. Let's study a little. See what I can get through your head—if anything."

Another middy said, "Aw, don't bully him, Matthews! He's doing all right!"

But Glasgow knew he wasn't doing all right. School was dull. Some of it didn't even make sense. He'd be glad when they weighed anchor— when he was at sea with some real things to learn!

6. FIRE DRILL

At the first note of the bosun's pipe Glasgow was awake. He heard Kingsbury's bellow routing out the sailors who swung their hammocks in the cramped space forward on the berth deck. According to ship routine, the midshipmen could sleep another hour.

If we're deaf, Glasgow thought. You could hear Kingsbury's bellow from the bottom of the hold to the top of the main topmast!

"All hands! Up hammocks!" Kingsbury roared. "Shake a leg there!" A thud, a curse, and the rumble of Kingsbury's laughter. He had dumped some laggard out of his hammock. The man was still swearing, but he was half laughing too.

Odd how the men liked Kingsbury. They hated the other two bosun's mates. Yet any of them swung the cat-o'-nine-tails when a man was flogged. And all of them carried the colt—a length of rope coiled in the crowns of their hats. Any sailor who dawdled might feel the sting of a colt across his shoulders.

If an officer said, "Start that man!" the bosun's mate on duty said, "Aye, aye, sir!" He snaked out the colt and delivered a lash with the full sweep of his arm.

There won't be much dawdling today, Glasgow thought. Today we sail!

At five bells of the forenoon watch, the whole crew—more than three hundred officers and men —were topside, with four side boys at the gangway, ready to pipe the captain aboard.

At a signal they piped, and Captain Porter came aboard. How handsome he looked in his new uniform. He returned the salutes and faced his crew. His speech was like his stride, brisk and decisive.

They were going on a training cruise, he said. He intended that the *Essex* should be the smartest ship in Commodore Rodgers' squadron. Training would be long and hard. That was the price of being the smartest ship in the squadron.

The men cheered; the band played. The captain smiled, spoke to Mr. Downes, and went below.

The First lifted his trumpet. "All hands, up anchor, ahoy!"

56

Pipes shrilled. Sailors lay below to man the capstan. The middies shouted every order after the First. Glasgow shouted as loud as he could. Someone sniggered. Glasgow's voice hadn't changed yet. Sometimes he sounded like a confounded girl. He clenched his fists and kept on yelling.

Presently every sail was loosed and sheeted home. The *Essex* was under way. Glasgow looked up. What a beautiful sight—all those white sails! His chest felt too big for his ribs.

"You seem to know those orders, Farragut," Mr. Downes said.

"I've been studying them since I was a little boy, sir."

"How old are you now?"

"Ten, sir."

"*Hmmm.* You know, Farragut, it wouldn't surprise me if you were a captain before you're thirty."

"Thank you, sir."

"You're to report to the captain, Farragut."

"Aye, aye, sir." What was it? A bawling-out about the ruckus on the wharf?

The captain was writing at a big table with a dozen chairs around it. What a big room. Fifteen feet deep and reaching clear across the ship. Glasgow thought of the cramped space forward on the berth deck where more than two hundred sailors swung their hammocks.

The captain looked up and smiled. "At ease, Glasgow."

Not a word about the ruckus on the wharf. Glasgow relaxed.

"I've special duty for you. You'll be captain's aide. Carry messages for me."

"Aye, aye, sir."

"You haven't seen my quarters yet, have you?" He got up and nodded toward the four cannons lashed to starboard and port, two on each side. "Part of our broadside. That forward wall is a bulkhead. When we clear for action the wall comes *out* and the gun crews come *in*." He led the way aft to another cabin, not so big as the first but nice and light, with windows across the stern. He opened the doors starboard and port. They each led to a smaller cabin with a bunk and chest of drawers and a bath off of it. They went back to the forward cabin.

What a lot of room for one man!

He had forgotten how the captain could read his mind. "A lot of room for one man, eh? But my sailing master spreads his charts here three times a day to plot our course. If the *Essex* is ever flagship of a squadron, a commodore will come aboard and take over everything but one stateroom.

58

"Yes, sir. I see, sir." But he still thought about the space where all the sailors swung their hammocks.

That afternoon Mr. Downes ordered gun drill. He appointed captains for each gun crew and midshipmen to work with them. The sailors counted off, a dozen men to each crew.

Lieutenant Block had a lantern jaw and narrow eyes. He looked Glasgow up and down. He sighed. "Well, come along."

I'll show him! Glasgow said to himself. He didn't know the orders for handling guns yet. But he could learn. All he had to do was listen and repeat what he heard.

Down on the gun deck though, with all the captains of the gun crews shouting and the crews lunging across the deck, handling their gun to starboard and then the opposite gun to port, Glasgow blundered around in a daze. He got behind the gun, and men hauling it in bumped him; he scuttled toward the muzzle, and men hauling on the tackles to aim it bumped him; he stood clear of everything and was knocked flat when the crew lunged across the deck to man the port gun.

When drill ended, Mr. Block looked at him and sighed again. "How old are you, Farragut?"

"Ten, sir."

"*Hmmm.* At the rate you're going you'll still be

a midshipman when you're thirty." He strode away.

Kingsbury ambled past Glasgow. "Someday," he rumbled softly, "Mr. Block might be standing under an open hatch when a marlinespike falls . . . sir."

Glasgow kept a straight face and eyes front, but he grinned when he told Matthews about it. Then he heaved a sigh. "Man, I'm tired!"

"Wait till we start adding other drills. Then you *will* be tired. Especially when we start training to board a ship. Hand-to-hand combat."

"What do we fight with?"

"Swords and dirks mostly. That's what we'll be drilled in."

Was Matthews joking? Their swords were sharp as razors. Their dirks—the blacksmith made them out of files—were even more deadly!

"No, Farragut," Matthews said, "we don't train with them. We'd kill off half the crew. We train with singlesticks, made of wood."

"That's a relief."

"Don't think it's easy. You'll drill till your right arm falls out of its socket. You'll pick it up, put it back, and go right on drilling."

Glasgow laughed. But after the first drill with singlesticks, he decided Matthews hadn't stretched it much. His right arm didn't fall out of its socket; it just felt like it might.

After drill with the guns and the singlesticks was well under way, Mr. Downes said, "Now we'll start boxing. That's vital. You might lose your sword or your dirk, but so long as you're conscious, you have your fists." Rubbing his chin, he eyed Glasgow. "We've no one to pair with him. So don't *pound* him; just *flick* him. But if you touch him, it counts."

Channing saluted and said helpfully, "I've had quite a bit of training in boxing, sir. I believe I can help Farragut without hurting him."

Glasgow knew what was coming, and it did. Channing did not use his fists, but some of his "flicks" were stiff-fingered jabs. Glasgow came out of the first session with a cut lip—Channing was "so sorry"—and assorted black-and-blue places.

That evening Kingsbury ambled by and spoke in his soft rumble. "Someday, Mr. Channing might be standing under an open hatch . . . sir."

One day Mr. Downes said, "Now we'll start fire drill."

Fire drill? Fire drill on a ship at sea? The men looked at one another with puzzled smiles.

Mr. Downes explained. A wooden ship with many coats of paint could burn like kindling. The rigging, soaked with tar, could burn like a torch. "And," he finished, "if the fire reached the magazines and our powder exploded . . ." He shrugged.

He assigned every man to a fire station: some to

the magazines to wet down the curtains in front of the doorways and four crews to man each pump, for the pumps would have to be kept working at top speed. Even if one crew collapsed, and a second crew collapsed on top of them, the pumps must not stop. There were double crews to handle the heavy hoses. Other men were stationed all over the ship to beat out sparks before they could start a blaze.

The men listened; they practiced running to their stations. Then fire drills started, and the grumbling began. For Captain Porter generally ordered fire drill in the middle of the night.

"Fire! Fire!" And every man must dash to his post.

It wasn't so bad for the watch on duty, but the watch off duty, in their hammocks, drugged with tiredness—they hated it. Day by day the grumbling got louder.

Glasgow writhed inside at the things they were saying about Captain Porter. But fire drill in the middle of a night was a lowdown trick!

Then one night there was the yell, "Fire! Fire!" and it was a fire! Glasgow could smell the smoke. He had never moved so fast in his life. It seemed to him he was at his station before his feet hit the deck.

The bosun's pipe signaled "general muster." What in the name of sense? The men left their fire stations and went topside. Smoke still rose from below.

Captain Porter faced them, then nodded to a man. "All right. Douse the smudge pots."

"Aye, aye, sir!" Four men went below. Soon the smoke died down.

Smudge pots! The captain had tricked them! A guttural mutter ran through the men. Glasgow's scalp crawled. He had never heard a sound so full of hate.

The captain faced their glares and glared back. "All right! I have seen just how fast you can move. Now hear this! Any time we have fire drill, if you're not at your stations that fast, you'll get a taste of the cat! Dismissed!"

The next day a worried-looking Kingsbury ambled past Glasgow. "If I was the captain, I sure wouldn't stand under an open hatch."

Near the end of their training cruise they rendezvoused with Commodore Rodgers. The big man came aboard, eyed the crew from under his shaggy eyebrows, and watched them go through maneuvers.

When he had gone, the pipes signaled "All hands on deck."

With blank faces and sullen eyes the men faced their captain. How, Glasgow wondered, could he stand to live with this feeling in the air?

The captain was brisk and casual. "First, I want

to thank you. Commodore Rodgers tells me the *Essex* is the smartest ship in the squadron. The best-trained crew in every respect!"

The men cheered—not heartily—but they did cheer.

"From here on because you are so well-trained, we shall have three watches instead of two—four hours on and eight hours off."

More cheers—a little louder.

"One thing more. I know how crowded the crew's quarters are on the forward part of the berth deck. Hereafter, you will swing your hammocks on the gun deck. When the gun ports can be open, you'll have decent ventilation. Even if the gun ports are closed, you'll have more room."

This time the cheers were really loud, and smiles went with them. Glasgow was so happy he had a lump in his throat. Since fire drills started nobody had had a good word to say for the captain—just mumble and mutter, grumble and grouse. Now all that would be wiped out. Maybe the captain was a stern leader, but he was a kind and thoughtful one too.

That night again the yell, "Fire! Fire!"

There was quite a bit of confusion because the men weren't used to swinging their hammocks on the gun deck.

Captain Porter bawled them out. Another drill

that sloppy, and he'd spread-eagle the crew and masthead the officers!

Heartsick, Glasgow heard the sullen muttering spread over the ship again.

Matthews was worried too. "I don't understand it! Farragut, if Captain Porter doesn't stop these infernal fire drills, he'll be the most hated man in the navy!"

7. WAR!

In June of 1812 the *Essex* was in port for overhaul —a slow business. The men were still muttering about fire drill and dragging their feet. Then the news came: America was at war with the British! Men who had poked about began to run.

July 3, the side boys piped Captain Porter aboard.

"Our orders," he said, "are to cruise offshore, on the lookout for enemy ships. When we meet one, we capture her!"

Wild cheers at that.

Glasgow understood. If the *Essex* captured an enemy ship, the captured ship was a prize. The captain would send a prize master and prize crew to take charge of her and to sail her to an American port. When the captured ship was sold, every man on the *Essex* would get a share of the prize money.

Navy duty in peacetime meant long hours, hard work, and low pay. But in wartime there was always the hope of prize money. So the men cheered.

The captain smiled, waited for silence, then explained what they were up against. Most of the guns of the *Essex* were carronades—very effective at close range, but no good otherwise.

"If a British ship armed with long eighteens sighted us *and recognized us for what we are*, she could sink us before we could bring a gun to bear. I have used every argument I can think of with the Navy Department to have the carronades changed for long-range guns. They refuse."

For a moment he stood, grim-faced, silent. Suddenly he smiled and went on. "So we shall have to substitute cunning for cannons! We'll not fly our ensign till we're ready for action. When we sight an enemy ship, we may throw out drags to cut our speed and trim our sails in such a lubberly fashion we'll be mistaken for a merchant vessel. Our sails will look sloppy enough to break a navy man's heart. Until the enemy is within our reach! Then —up with the ensign! Out with the guns! And we'll hull the enemy with the first broadside!"

Thunderous cheers.

A tingle crawled up Glasgow's spine. This was real. When the drums beat to quarters now, it would not be drill. It would be war. How would he feel? When battle came, what would he do?

Two days later he reported to the captain's cabin. "You sent for me, sir?"

The captain grinned. "Yes, Glasgow. To congratulate you. You are now—how is it you say it—'going-on-twelve.' "

July the fifth. His birthday. "I had forgotten."

"A lot to think about?"

"Yes, sir."

"About what it will be like when battle comes?"

"Yes, sir."

"I remember when I was facing my first action. The waiting is always lots harder than the action."

"It is, sir?"

"It's this way, Glasgow. If someone you loved were in danger, would you think of yourself or the person you loved?"

"I *hope* I'd think of that person!"

The captain nodded. "When battle comes, your ship is in danger. And you'll be so busy trying to save her that you won't think about yourself. You understand?"

Glasgow wasn't sure he did, but he said, "Yes, sir. Thank you, sir."

Then Captain Porter did a startling thing. He

sighed and slumped in his chair, his head bowed. It was the first time Glasgow had ever seen him look tired or discouraged.

"You've nothing to worry about," the captain said grimly. "I'll worry enough for all of us."

"Sir! What's wrong?"

"Everything! We haven't had a Congress since the beginning that knew how important a navy is! President Washington knew. He was an army man, but he understood. I've read what he said to Congress clear back in 1796: 'To secure respect for a neutral flag requires a naval force, organized and ready to vindicate it from insult or aggression.' But what do we do? Wait till war is on our doorstep and *then* start to get ready! We've declared war against England. What have we got to fight with? About twenty ships that can keep the sea. For the rest, nothing but those stupid little shallow-draft gunboats." He sighed again. "This is going to be a devil of a war."

"But, sir! When you talked to the men, you sounded like we could—could lick anything!"

The captain smiled wryly. "Of course. And I'll keep on talking to them that way. Why? Because they are followers. That's all the most of them will ever be." He looked squarely at Glasgow. "But you have the stuff of a leader! So I thought you ought to know what you may be up against. Just because our people don't know that a strong navy is the best way to keep the peace and the only way to win a war."

Glasgow's head was swimming. He only said, "Yes, sir."

Then the captain shrugged off his black mood. "Don't worry about what you'll do when you face action, lad. Even if you're scared, you'll be too proud to show it."

Glasgow remembered Nancy and that sail with Father in the whipping wind and flying spray. How long ago it seemed. Like another life.

"Sail ho-o-o-o-o! Sail ho-o-o-o-o to starboard!"

Almost before the lookout's singsong cry died, Mr. Downes was snapping orders. Pipes shrilled; drums beat.

The gun crews cleared for action but left the gun ports closed. Other men put out drags. Topmen lay aloft to loose more sail, as though trying to escape.

Another cry from the lookout. The ship had changed course and was heading toward the *Essex*. The gun crews on the spar deck crouched behind the bulwarks, hidden, waiting.

Another hail from the lookout. The ship was British.

Soon the *Alert* bore down upon them, guns

bristling. She fired a shot across the bow of the *Essex*, signaling her to heave to. Sailors on the *Alert* shouted taunts:

"Surrender, you Yankee traders!"

"Nation of shopkeepers!"

"Cowards!"

On the *Essex*, pipes shrilled. Up went her ensign. That was greeted with more jeers from the *Alert*:

"Hooray!"

"They think they want to fight!"

"Let them have it!"

Before the British were done jeering, the *Essex* was in action: gun ports open, guns run out and fired. The *Essex* wore around and loosed another broadside.

Glasgow saw panic on the *Alert*—gun crews fleeing from their posts and diving down hatchways. In eight minutes the *Alert* surrendered.

Captain Porter sent Lieutenant Finch and a prize crew to the *Alert* and boats to bring prisoners from the *Alert* to the *Essex*.

The British came aboard in a daze, muttering:

"We heard you Yankees were just merchant cowards."

"That you were afraid to fight."

"We didn't know you *could* fight."

"Well, now you know!" Kingsbury bellowed, and the sailors of the *Essex* shouted with laughter.

"I wasn't scared at all!" Glasgow told himself. "Not a bit!"

But that night when he shut his eyes, he could see the action all over again. He was a long time getting to sleep. The next day was all right. But the second night was as bad as the first. He lay with his eyes shut, breathing evenly, trying to force himself to calm down and go to sleep.

Suddenly he had a feeling that someone was standing over him. He slitted his eyes to look out. Moonlight came through a hatchway and revealed the coxswain of the *Alert*, standing near him, with a pistol in his hand. Mutiny! The prisoners had escaped and were going to take over the ship!

Glasgow forced himself to lie still and breathe evenly. At last the coxswain crept forward and disappeared in the shadows.

Glasgow swung down from his hammock and tiptoed to the captain's cabin. He entered, felt his way to the captain's bunk, and whispered, "It's Glasgow, sir!"

The captain moved. Glasgow knew he was awake. "What is it, lad?"

"The prisoners. They're going to mutiny, sir. The coxswain was by my hammock with a pistol."

"Good lad!" Captain Porter leaped from his bunk, grabbed a trumpet, and dashed out on the gun deck. "Fire! Fire!"

Every *Essex* man was at his station on the double. The prisoners milled around in confusion. It did not take long to overpower them. Mr. Downes found the two guards that the prisoners had knocked out. He stationed four guards this time with orders not to turn their backs.

The next day the *Essex* was full of laughter and bragging. The men who had grumbled most about fire drills bragged the loudest:

"A clever business, all right!"

"I always said the captain knew what he was about!"

"Yes, sir! A man'd have to get up mighty early to get ahead of Captain Porter!"

"No wonder we're the smartest ship in the navy!"

By noon someone had heard about Glasgow's part in warning the captain. Most of the middies laughed and slapped him on the back.

Only Channing sneered. "Our hero! How did you manage to keep so still you fooled the coxswain, Farragut?"

"I think I was too scared to move," Glasgow said.

The others stared at him.

"Funny. I was scared *before* the battle, and *after* the battle, more than right *in* the battle. I think maybe I was scared some in the battle. Scared, but too proud to show it."

A moment of silence. All the middies but Channing looked at one another and began to grin. Then —the older ones first—they admitted they knew the feeling—"scared and too proud to show it."

"And anybody," Matthews declared, "who says he never was afraid is a liar!"

8. ALONE IN THE
SOUTH PACIFIC

After ten weeks the *Essex* returned to New York for supplies. Crowds lined the wharves to cheer. The prize ships she had sent home had spread the word. Nine prizes in ten weeks!

A boat brought a letter for the captain. Glasgow took it to his cabin.

The captain read it and whistled. "Get Downes here on the double!"

The next time Glasgow was in the cabin the big table was covered with papers. "All that," the captain was saying, "and anything else we can stow!"

What in the world? All those supplies. The *Essex* must be going on a very long cruise.

Captain Porter and Glasgow went home to Chester for a few days. William was toddling around now. He had a baby sister, Elizabeth. Glasgow thought of his own little sister. When would he ever see her again?

Long after he had gone to bed that first night in Chester, Glasgow heard the rumble of the captain's voice. Was he telling Mrs. Porter about the long cruise they were to make? The next morning at breakfast Mrs. Porter's eyes were frightened. Yes, the captain must have told her.

Back on the *Essex* again, Glasgow could feel the excitement running through the crew. Where were they going?

When they were well at sea Captain Porter told them. They would rendezvous with two other ships under Commodore Bainbridge. The three ships would go where no ship of their navy had ever been before—around Cape Horn, into the South Pacific. They would protect American whalers and merchant ships; they would capture British ships!

Prizes! The men cheered.

"First rendezvous, Porto Praya in the Cape Verde Islands!" the captain said. "Commodore Bainbridge will wait for us there until November twenty-fifth. Let's beat him into port! Let's be waiting for him when he arrives!"

More cheers. With all sails taut the *Essex* sped along.

That night a savage storm struck her. For three days the *Essex* wallowed. It was November 25, the last day Bainbridge would wait for them, when the *Essex* stood off Porto Praya. No sign of the *Constitution* or the *Hornet.*

Mr. Downes went ashore for news and came back looking grim. No American ships had been there for weeks.

What had happened, Glasgow wondered. Had the other ships been captured? Or caught in a storm and sunk?

Pipes called all hands on deck. Captain Porter faced them with his usual brisk confidence. Evidently Bainbridge had been delayed. When he could not reach Porto Praya in time, he had gone on to the second rendezvous. He'd be waiting for them there. That, the captain said, was why they had more than one rendezvous.

The men nodded. But they were not smiling.

The *Essex* took on water and fresh provisions and sailed.

A few days later the lookout's cry drifted down. "Sail ho-o-o-o-o!"

The British merchant ship *Nocton* clapped on sail and fled.

"She'll not escape us!" Mr. Downes. said. "We can outsail any merchant ship in the world!"

They overtook the *Nocton* and fired one shot

across her bow. She surrendered. She carried $50,000 in gold.

Captain Porter relieved her of her cargo and sent a prize crew to take her to the United States. The men of the *Essex* strutted and laughed. What a lucky ship the *Essex* was! A few more prizes like that, and they'd all be rich!

But late in January, and hundreds of miles to the south, the men had lost their smiles and their swagger. No sign of Bainbridge at any rendezvous. What now?

Glasgow watched Captain Porter pacing his cabin, head bowed, frowning. What was he thinking?

"My compliments to Mr. Downes, Farragut," the captain said. "I want all hands on deck."

"Aye, aye, sir."

The captain had no troubled frown when he faced his men. He smiled. The *Essex*, he said, would complete her tour of duty. She would go into the Pacific alone!

The men cheered. They did not stop smiling even when the captain told them of the problems they faced. And they did have problems: They were low on provisions. Even when they cut rations in half, their food would last only three months. It could take that long—even longer—to beat their way around Cape Horn against head winds.

"Of course," he went on, "when we are in the Pacific, we'll have no problem about provisions. I expect to keep us supplied from the prizes we take!"

More cheers. The men strutted. What a ship! What a captain!

Later Glasgow found the captain sitting slumped in his chair, staring at nothing. *Why was he going alone into the Pacific?*

The captain looked up and answered the question Glasgow had not asked. "I'm going on because it's the only thing to do. We haven't provisions enough to get home. There is nowhere safe to try to provision the *Essex.* The coast off the United States is probably swarming with British ships by now." He sighed. "This is a devil of a war."

But the next day, cool, confident, smiling, he stood on deck, watching the preparations for the battle against Cape Horn weather. Men cleared the guns from the spar deck and stowed them in the hold. There must be no extra weight topside when a ship rolled, scuppers under. They double-lashed the guns in the hold. They double-lashed the guns on the main deck too. If a gun broke loose in a storm, there would be smashed bulkheads and broken arms and legs before they could secure it again. They checked every inch of the standing and running rigging; they bent on new

79

sails; they broke out the heaviest clothes for the men.

Soon fitful winds and sudden storms kept the topmen fighting to handle wet, heavy sails with fingers almost too numb to hold on.

"Cheer up, my laddies!" Kingsbury yelled. "You're just getting in practice for Cape Horn weather! The worst is yet to come!"

Then Cape Horn weather hit them. Soon they were flying nothing but a reefed foresail and close-reefed main topsail. Later they stripped the *Essex* to nothing but storm staysails. Even then she rolled so violently that she threatened to snap her masts with every lurch.

They steered farther south. "It's a tossup," Kingsbury said. "Stand too far south, you'll hit icebergs. Don't stand far enough south, and you may go aground."

At sixty degrees south they should have found calmer weather. They did not. All February they fought head winds, sleety rains, and dangerous seas. They did manage to keep the *Essex* close enough to the wind to make a westing.

February ended. The sea grew more calm. The crew had time to catch a breath. The officers talked of what they'd do to harass the enemy in the Pacific. Was it time now to bring the guns up from the hold so they'd be ready for action?

Then the most savage storm of all struck them.

Mountainous seas washed over the deck. The pumps were choked. It was impossible to keep water from flooding the hold.

Glasgow saw the officers cast anxious looks at the masts every time the *Essex* heeled over and snapped back again.

The men knew what threatened too. They fought to tighten the standing rigging to steady the masts. They ran a lifeline, waist-high, the length of the spar deck for men to hang onto when they went forward or aft. In spite of the lifeline a dozen men fell and crashed into bulwarks. The surgeon and his mates were busy setting broken bones.

"One thing," Mr. Downes said, "this storm can't last much longer. It'll blow itself out. We ought to see a change by tomorrow."

They did. The storm got worse. Finally the mightiest wave of all broke over the *Essex* and stove in all gun ports on the weather side. Two boats ripped loose and went overboard. The head rail and hammock stanchions on the weather side went. Another boat tore loose and smashed into the helm. Water poured down into the ship, flooding the hold and sloshing over the berth deck.

For the first time Glasgow saw strong, experienced sailors panic. They gave up completely, knelt, and began to pray.

Kingsbury stumbled up from below, and his

bellow was louder than the storm. "Damn your eyes! Step lively! We've still got *one* side of her left!"

His bellow brought the men out of their shock. They managed to cover the gun ports. Good swimmers took turns diving below till the pumps were cleared. They got the waterlogged, wallowing *Essex* under control.

The next day the sea was calm. For the first time in almost two months they had good weather.

By the middle of March they were shipshape again, sailing under clear skies toward the harbor of Valparaiso in Chile.

Glasgow heard Captain Porter and the First talking about Chile. The Spanish were siding with the British in the war. Would Chile follow her mother country and side with the British too?

It was a risk to put into port, but they needed provisions. So the *Essex* stood in toward shore. There was not much of a harbor at Valparaiso. Just an open bay, protected from the south winds by a tongue of land.

"So long as the wind's from the south," Mr. Downes said, "it's safe enough."

"But if the wind comes from any other direction," the captain said, "heaven help a ship in port!"

Mr. Downes went ashore to sound out the mood

82

of Chile. He came back smiling. Chile had rebelled against Spain. She was ready to side with
the United States. Governor Lastre would help the
Essex in every way possible. He was sending a
messenger to Santiago to tell Mr. Poinsett, Consul-
General from the United States, that Captain
Porter was in Valparaiso.

Wild yells on the spar deck interrupted Mr.
Downes. Glasgow dashed topside; the captain and
the First followed. Sailors crowded the bulwarks
and the rigging, looking down into the water.
Glasgow climbed where he could see too. Laughing men were bringing boatloads of fruit to the
Essex. Glasgow saw melons, peaches, apples, and
half a dozen fruits he did not know.

"A present from Governor Lastre!" a boatman
yelled. "To our brave amigos."

"Tomorrow," Mr. Downes said, "we can start
loading provisions. Governor Lastre promised all
the supplies and all the help we need. I told him
we'd pay for provisions with good English gold,
courtesy of the *Nocton*!"

Glasgow took a deep breath. What a lucky ship
the *Essex* was. The terrors of Cape Horn were forgotten—almost. Sometimes he still wakened in a
sweat and wondered if he had yelled.

When the *Essex* was provisioned, she sailed.
People of Valparaiso lined the shore and perched

on rooftops to cheer her on her way.

"Once more," the captain said, "we'll have to substitute cunning for cannons."

Twice the *Essex* lured a British ship close enough to take her. Then they took a smart little vessel that pleased the captain. He armed her with carronades from the other prizes, renamed her the *Essex Junior*, and put Mr. Downes in charge.

Now, Glasgow thought, our captain is commanding a squadron. From now on he is Commodore Porter!

He smiled to himself—then sobered as Mr. Downes picked his crew, for Mr. Downes was taking William Kingsbury.

"I'll miss you," Glasgow told him. "You're—I feel like you're my best friend on the *Essex*."

"That's because I've known you longer than anyone, lad," Kingsbury said. Generally he remembered to add "sir," but this time he didn't. "I fought with your father! I'm the one that knows you're the son of a hero!"

Glasgow's scalp tingled. He swallowed hard against a lump in his throat. "I wish you weren't going to be so far away."

Kingsbury's chuckle rumbled. "I'll not be far. Even if the *Essex* and the *Essex Junior* were a mile apart, I could still hail you without a trumpet!"

Glasgow had to laugh at that. "Kingsbury, what were you like when you were my size?"

84

Kingsbury rubbed his chin. "Hanged if I remember. I ain't even sure I ever was that small. You're a nubbin' for sure. But you're the son of a hero! Don't ever forget that, lad! The stuff is there . . . sir!" Then he saluted and went over the side to the boat that would take him to the *Essex Junior*.

The next day the *Essex* took another prize. The day after—still another. Sometimes when she challenged a ship the crew met her with cheers. Many of the men were American sailors who had been seized by the British and forced to serve on British ships.

"If we take many more prizes," the captain said, "I'll run out of prize masters. I may have to make cartel ships of my prizes." Then he explained. "I'll parole the captain and crew. They'll give their word not to fight again until they've been exchanged. I'll give the captain papers explaining where his ship is bound for. All ships, British and American, are supposed to let him pass. Sort of a gentleman's agreement."

Glasgow bristled. "A gentleman's agreement! When we're fighting a war! When we're fighting like tigers to save our country?"

"You have a lot to learn," Captain Porter said.

"I guess I do!" Glasgow muttered.

It was July 9 before he remembered that his birthday had come and gone. He was twelve-going-on-thirteen. He laughed to himself. What was a

85

mere birthday to a man who was sailing with the smartest ship in the U.S. Navy?

That afternoon Captain Porter called all his fleet together. He had eleven ships now—nine prizes, the *Essex*, and the *Essex Junior*. He signaled for two men to come to the *Essex*: Mr. Downes and Captain Randall, master of a whaler that was one of their prizes.

First, the captain talked with Mr. Downes. The fleet would be divided here: The *Essex* would sail north to keep an eye out for more prizes, and the *Essex Junior* would take five of the prizes to Valparaiso to dispose of them.

Mr. Downes saluted and returned to the *Essex Junior*.

Captain Porter turned to Captain Randall of the *Barclay*. Randall was a huge, grizzled fellow with a mean mouth.

"Who is your navigator?" Captain Porter asked.

Captain Randall looked at his fist. "He was a troublemaker. I got rid of him."

"Then I'll leave you aboard to navigate the *Barclay*," Captain Porter said. "But the ship will be under the command of my prize master. You understand?"

"Aye," Captain Randall snarled. "Who's your prize master . . . sir?"

"Mr. Farragut," Captain Porter said.

9. PRIZE MASTER

Prize master! Glasgow didn't know how long he stood in a daze. He heard Captain Porter say, "Help Mr. Farragut with his gear."

"Aye, aye, sir!" The sailor was as big as Hawley had been. He faced Glasgow, touched his forelock, and waited.

Glasgow snapped out of his daze and went below.

The sailor followed him in silence. When they were in the steerage, he said, "That Randall, he's a mighty mean-looking man, sir."

Glasgow had been thinking the same thing. He only smiled, shrugged, and fumbled in his chest for what he'd take with him. Why couldn't he collect his wits?

"I—I hope he doesn't try to make any trouble, sir."

"He won't!" Glasgow said. "He won't dare. I'll be in charge." He hoped he sounded more sure than he felt. Why couldn't he collect his wits? He went back to his chest three times to put something in and take something else out.

"Yes, sir. I mean, no, sir. I guess you're right, sir." The sailor sounded doubtful.

"There! That's ready!"

"Aye, aye, sir." The sailor picked up Glasgow's gear and followed him.

When they got topside, the *Essex Junior* and four of the prize ships were already under way. The *Barclay* was standing by. Captain Randall and part of the prize crew had already gone aboard. Three more men waited in a boat for Mr. Farragut, prize master. Glasgow did not know them; they were prisoners from prize ships who had volunteered to serve on the *Essex*. What would they think of serving under him?

The *Essex* was ready to sail. Topmen were aloft, ready to handle the sails.

Captain Porter said, "You'll overtake the *Essex Junior* without any trouble, Mr. Farragut!"

"Aye, aye, sir!" He forced a smile, squared his

shoulders, and took his place in the boat. As the boat pulled for the *Barclay*, the *Essex* and her prize ships headed north.

Nobody piped the prize master aboard. The sailors stood around, shooting sidelong glances at Captain Randall. Evidently he had been talking.

Glasgow scanned the horizon: The *Essex* was speeding north, the *Essex Junior* now far to the south. The *Barclay* was alone.

Glasgow swallowed hard, then lifted his trumpet. "I want that main topsail filled! Close up with the *Essex Junior*!"

Captain Randall ripped out a string of oaths, then yelled, "I'll shoot the first man that touches a rope without my orders!" He felt for his pistols, missed them, and dived below to his cabin.

The prize crew stood motionless, looking at the very small midshipman. Glasgow looked at them and could not call one man by name. If only he had Hawley or Kingsbury or somebody he knew!

He lifted his trumpet again. "I want that main topsail filled!"

A moment of silence. Then one of the prize crew saluted, grinned, and yelled, "Aye, aye, sir!"

All the men came alive. Topmen lay aloft. Glasgow let out his breath in a shuddering sigh. He realized he had held it so long his chest ached. One after another he gave his orders. Soon the

Barclay had way on and was closing with the other ships.

Glasgow sent a man below. "Tell Captain Randall if he comes topside with arms, it's mutiny. He'll go overboard!"

"Aye, aye, sir!"

After a while Randall did come on deck. He was still glowering, but he did not carry his pistols, and he did not try to give any orders.

When the *Barclay* overtook the *Essex Junior*, Kingsbury hailed them. He had said he could hail a ship without a trumpet. He could. Prize Master Farragut and Captain Randall would report to the *Essex Junior*.

As a boat took them to the *Essex Junior*, Randall wet his lips nervously. Twice he cleared his throat as though about to say something. Once he even tried to smile.

Mr. Downes waited for them on deck. "What was the delay, Mr. Farragut?"

"Captain Randall tried to countermand my orders, sir. He swore he would shoot the first man who touched a rope. He went below for his pistols."

Mr. Downes stared at the grizzled captain. "Well, sir?"

Randall managed a sickly smile. "I didn't mean anything. I was just trying to scare the little fellow."

90

Mr. Downes' voice dripped ice. "You were trying to do what?"

"To scare the—the—Mr. Farragut."

"That's better! See that you remember that name. *Mr. Farragut!*"

Glasgow would have liked to jump up and down and whoop. He didn't. He stood, feet spread, hands behind him, head up, chin in. "Ask him, sir, if he thinks he did scare me."

"Well, Randall?"

Randall's eyes blazed, but his mouth wore the sickly smile. "No, sir. I didn't scare him, sir."

Mr. Downes stared at Randall long and hard. Then he said, "Mr. Farragut, I don't think you'll need a navigator. I'm sure you can keep your station with the rest of the squadron. Shall I just hold Randall here and throw him in chains?"

It was a temptation. But Glasgow said, "No, sir. That won't be necessary. Let him come back to the *Barclay*."

"If there's any trouble . . ."

"There won't be, sir."

And there wasn't.

Glasgow learned what the saying that "a captain sleeps with one eye open" meant. He felt that he slept "with one eye open" all the way to Valparaiso. He was on deck at almost any hour, giving commands, keeping the *Barclay* just astern

91

and to the port side of the *Essex Junior*. What fun
it was to be in command! To give orders and see
his ship obey! *His* ship! Of course, she was nothing
but a whaler. But someday he'd command a real
ship!

When they were anchored off Valparaiso, Mr.
Downes sent for Glasgow again. He returned
Glasgow's salute, then shook hands. "Well done,
Mr. Farragut! Well done! I'll make a full report to
Captain Porter! That the youngest middy ever to
command a prize ship handled her like an old sea
dog!"

"Thank you, sir."

"How old are you, Farragut?"

"Twelve, sir. July the fifth."

"We missed celebrating your birthday!"

"Oh, that!" Glasgow shrugged. "I just thought
about birthdays when I was a little boy."

Mr. Downes smiled. Then he said, "Governor
Lastre has invited me and all my prize masters to
dinner tonight. You'll be ready at six bells."

"Aye, aye, sir!"

*Mr. Farragut, prize master! Dining with the
governor!*

That evening Governor Lastre looked a little
puzzled when he saw Glasgow. He turned to Mr.
Downes. "Your son, perhaps?"

"Prize master of the *Barclay*. And Mr. Farragut

92

handled his ship like an old sea dog. The *Barclay* kept her station off my port side all the way."

"*Por dios!*" the governor said.

Glasgow remembered that Father used to say that when he got excited.

When Mr. Downes had disposed of all his prize ships, he transferred the prize crews to the *Essex Junior*. Before they sailed, he told them every man would have leave on shore. The men cheered, drew straws for which watch got the first leave, and the lucky ones went ashore.

But later that day a boat brought news to Mr. Downes. A messenger had come across the Andes from the east coast of South America. A British squadron was on its way around Cape Horn to capture the *Essex*.

Signal guns called all men back to the *Essex Junior*. They came, puzzled, scowling. Nobody liked to have his promised shore leave cut short.

Mr. Downes gave them the news. "So we haven't a minute to waste! We don't know how soon the British will reach the Pacific. We've got to warn Captain Porter. So bear a hand, my hearties! We've got to get under way in jig time."

The sullen frowns faded. "Aye, aye, sir!"

Soon the *Essex Junior* was provisioned and sailing north to meet the *Essex*. What, Glasgow wondered, would Captain Porter do? Would he try to escape the British by sailing around Cape Horn? Or would he try to escape by sailing west, on around the world?

Captain Porter wasn't going to do either. He was going to do battle with the British. "But first," he said, "we've got to overhaul the *Essex* and put her in fighting trim. Her bottom is so foul it's taken four knots off her speed."

The *Essex*, the *Essex Junior*, and four prize ships sailed west to the Marquesas Islands and anchored off Nukuhiva. The natives were friendly. They swarmed out in dugout canoes to meet the ships.

Soon the overhauling began. Men built a shelter on the sandy beach and stored all guns, ammunition, and stores from the *Essex*. They removed top hamper—spars, sails, and running rigging. They put smudge pots in the hold to drive out rats. Then they dragged the empty hulk into shallow water. With stout cables they careened her so first one side and then the other was exposed. With torches and scrapers they cleaned the barnacles and filth from the hull. In less than six weeks she was ready for sea.

Captain Porter called his four prize masters together. "You'll stand by here at Nukuhiva. If you do not hear from me in three months, you'll take your prizes back to the United States." Then he smiled. "I expect to be back before then with a British ship or two in tow!"

The *Essex* and the *Essex Junior* sailed. They kept well out to sea until they were south of Valparaiso. The wind was generally from the south, the captain explained. If the British ships were at Valparaiso, he wanted the weather gage of them as he stood in to shore.

"If we catch them there, we'll have them, won't we, sir?" Glasgow said.

Captain Porter shook his head. "We can't attack an enemy ship in a neutral port. But if the British are there, I think they'll come out to meet me!" He looked pleased at the prospect.

When they reached Valparaiso there was no sign of the British. They had not come yet. The U.S. Consul-General, Mr. Poinsett, came to talk to Captain Porter. Did the captain think he could provision his ships and escape in time?

"I'm not trying to escape, Mr. Poinsett."

"Captain Porter!"

"The *Essex* can outsail and outmaneuver any ship in the British navy."

"But what can you do against more than one ship?"

"We can outmaneuver them too. I'll pretend to run from them. Their fastest ship will overtake me. When she's close enough, we'll open up with our carronades. She'll strike her colors before the other ships can join in the fight."

He ordered the *Essex Junior* to stand off the point of land to the south, on lookout for the British. When she sighted them, she would fire signal guns, then clap on sail and get back to the safety of the port. She would stay there until the *Essex* had dealt with the British. She did not have the speed to outmaneuver the British; she was not armed to do battle against a British broadside.

When the *Essex Junior* had sailed, the captain gave orders: The men would be drilled daily with singlesticks and boxing. So, Glasgow thought, the captain expects to board a British ship! Would the captain let him join the boarding party?

He was getting better at boxing now. His opponent might be a head taller and have a longer reach, but more and more often Glasgow ducked inside his guard and landed a blow.

Boarding . . . not with singlesticks, but with dirks and swords. Fighting to kill a man . . . He tried not to think about it.

Days dragged by. The people of Valparaiso were kind. They brought presents of fruit and livestock to the *Essex*. The steerage had a new pet—Murphy, a little white pig. He had been the runt of the litter so the middies hoped he wouldn't get too big too soon.

Governor Lastre entertained the officers with dinners and dances. Presently the captain said it was high time the *Essex* entertained the governor and his friends. He called the *Essex Junior* in from lookout duty and ordered the *Essex* decorated for a dance.

The night of the dance, old sailors shook their heads over dance music, decorations, and long tables with refreshments on the gun deck. A fine business on a ship of war!

It was late when the dance ended and the boats plied back and forth, carrying the guests ashore. The *Essex Junior* sailed back to her lookout station.

The sky was a pale before-dawn gray when the *Essex Junior* fired her warning shots. The one night she had not been on lookout duty the British had come!

On the *Essex* drums beat, pipes shrilled. For a time there was confusion as men clearing away after the dance got in the way of men clearing for action. But soon they were clearing for action on the double. They cast loose guns, removed bulkheads, opened gunports, and brought powder and shot from below. Four dozen men armed with dirks and swords were ready to board if the captain gave the word.

Soon the lookout reported: The *Essex Junior*, all

sails spread, was fleeing the British, fleeing to the safety of a neutral port.

"Farragut," the captain said, "check to see if the surgeon has everything he needs."

"Aye, aye, sir!" Glasgow hurried below to the berth deck and forward to a hatchway that led down into the cockpit. Matthews had said the cockpit had one advantage: It was below the waterline; in battle an enemy shot was not so apt to reach it. It was the only advantage, Glasgow thought, as he looked down into the gloomy space. Candlelight showed that the surgeon and his mates had their instruments laid out ready on the table.

No, the surgeon said, there was nothing else he needed. Glasgow hurried topside again. He wasn't going to miss anything!

About dawn two British ships appeared in the distance—the frigate *Phoebe* and the sloop *Cherub*. The *Phoebe* steered into the harbor, coming straight at the *Essex*. Her commander, a lean, gray man, lolled against a gun carriage on the spar deck, studying the *Essex*. The *Phoebe* was cleared for action. Had the British hoped to catch the *Essex* napping, not ready for battle? If they had caught her napping, would they have broken international law and attacked her in a neutral port?

The captain of the *Phoebe* scanned the *Essex*

and took in the facts with a quick glance. The *Essex* was ready for action too. He raised his hand in a languid salute. His ship was so close to the *Essex* that he could hail her without a trumpet.

"Captain Hillyar's compliments to Captain Porter. He hopes Captain Porter is well."

Glasgow saw Captain Porter lift a trumpet to answer. He did not need a trumpet to be heard by Captain Hillyar. Glasgow smiled to himself. What Captain Porter was going to say would be heard by every man on both ships!

"Quite well!" The captain's voice rang out. "But I hope you will not come too near. If you do, there might be an accident." One motion of his hand and four dozen men, armed to the teeth, crowded the fo'c'sle, ready to board.

Captain Hillyar lost his languid air. He stiffened and spoke quickly. If the *Phoebe* did fall aboard the *Essex*, it would be an accident—quite unintentional!

Captain Porter's voice boomed again. "You know you have no business where you are! Touch one rope—one yard—of the *Essex*, and we'll board you instantly!"

Glasgow clenched his fists. Please, please let the *Phoebe* touch us! She'll surrender in ten minutes!

But the *Phoebe*, her sails aback, managed to pass the *Essex* without touching her. She came to

99

anchor astern of the *Essex*—where the *Essex* could bring no guns to bear.

After the British had taken on supplies they stood offshore, but they stayed within sight of the harbor. The *Essex* and the *Essex Junior* were blockaded in port. If the *Essex* sailed out beyond the three-mile limit, the British with their long-range guns could riddle her before she could bring her carronades to bear. The six long-range guns on the *Essex* would not mean much against broadsides of long-range guns on the *Phoebe*.

Days dragged by. Captain Porter drilled his men and kept an eye on the British. What, Glasgow wondered, was he thinking?

Then a wild gale blew down through the hills to the east and hit the *Essex* with the fury of a hurricane. She lurched and strained at her cables. One cable snapped and the other anchor dragged. The *Essex* began to drift out from shore.

Captain Porter didn't waste any time making up his mind. "Cut the cable! Clap on sail! We're going to outrun the *Phoebe*!"

The east gale died down; the prevailing wind was from the south again. The *Phoebe* had the weather gage of the *Essex*. But Captain Porter spoke to the helmsmen. "Keep close to the wind as possible!"

The *Essex* was heading for the point of land to

the south. Once she rounded it, she could hope to outrun the British. Closer and closer to the point of land—Glasgow held his breath till his chest hurt, trying to will more speed into the *Essex*. Just a little farther and they would round the point! Just a little . . .

Then another squall, more violent than the first, roared down from the east. It hit the spread of sail on the *Essex*. She heeled over till her yards almost touched the water, then lurched back. From above came a sickening *Crack*! The main topmast snapped and fell into the sea. The topmen stationed there screamed, clutched air, and plummeted downward. The waves swallowed them.

What chance now to outsail the *Phoebe*? Captain Porter gave orders to come about and return to port, but in the teeth of the eastern gale they could not do it.

"If I can get her close enough to run her aground," he said, "and the men can escape, I'll burn her! She'll not fall into British hands!"

But he could not get that close inshore. He came to anchor more than three miles from the city but not quite a mile offshore. Was he close enough to be under the protection of a neutral port?

Evidently the British did not think so. The *Phoebe* and *Cherub*, colors flying, bore down on

the *Essex*. The *Phoebe* came in under the stern of
the *Essex*, where not one gun could be brought to
bear. She wore around and loosed a broadside of
long eighteens.

On the *Essex* masts splintered; yards crashed to
the deck; a gun exploded, killing half its crew.

Captain Porter yelled, "Farragut! To the gun
deck! Tell them to drag three long twelves aft!
Smash the stern windows and fire from there!"

"Aye, aye, sir!" He plunged down to the gun
deck and stumbled over a body. It was headless. For
one sick minute he shut his eyes and swallowed
hard. Then he yelled his message to the captain of
a gun crew and hurried topside.

A body fell at his feet—one of the powder boys.
Glasgow snatched up the leather powder bucket
and raced down to a magazine in the hold. A man
filled the bucket and jammed on the tight-fitting
lid. Glasgow started back.

The surgeon and his mates were operating on
the berth deck. The surgeon yelled, "Cockpit's too
crowded. Tell the captain!"

On the gun deck he heard Kingsbury's bellow
and stopped in surprise.

Kingsbury saw him and paused a moment. "The
Essex Junior can't get in the fight, but hanged if I
was going to miss it!" He turned aft again, and
Glasgow heard his exultant roar as a long twelve
from the *Essex* scored a hit on the *Phoebe*.

Glasgow went topside again. After that he lost track of time. The ship was an inferno of crashes, yells, and the screams of wounded men.

The *Phoebe* wore around again to where not a gun of the *Essex* could reach her. She was pouring red-hot shot into the *Essex* now. Smoke billowed up from below.

Kingsbury lunged topside, his clothing ablaze, and plunged over the side.

In a momentary silence Glasgow heard the captain say, "Poor devil, he'll never make it."

Now smoke billowed from every hatch, and flames leaped in the smoke. More men staggered topside, their clothing ablaze.

"It's hopeless, sir!" one gasped. "Surrender, sir! If we can't put out the fires before they reach the magazines, we'll all die!"

"Find the signal book, Farragut," the captain said. "Throw it overboard. It must not fall into enemy hands."

So . . . it was all over. They were going to surrender. Heartsick, Glasgow searched for the signal book, found it, threw it overboard, and watched it sink.

10. THE END OF THE *ESSEX*

Grim-faced, Captain Porter lowered the flag.

Pipes shrilled, calling men to fire stations. After a while the smoke wavered, then stopped. Men laid the dead in a row on the port side. Others carried the wounded below.

Now that it was all over, Glasgow realized he was shaking. After the first shock of seeing a man die, he could not remember feeling anything. He had just raced all over the ship, doing anything he saw to do. Now he was shaking. He took a deep breath and reported back to the captain.

"Think you could help the surgeon?" the captain asked.

"Yes, sir!"

"It's mighty grim duty for—"

"I'll be all right, sir!" After all, if a man could keep his nerve throughout a battle, he ought to be able to help the surgeon. He hurried below.

"Mr. Farragut reporting for . . ." He took one look around, then shut his eyes and grabbed something to steady himself.

"If you're going to faint, get out!" the surgeon barked.

"I'll be all right, sir."

"Next!" the surgeon said.

Four sailors heaved another man onto the table. The surgeon examined his arm. "That's got to come off. Get him ready."

One sailor gave the man a swallow of rum. Another gave him a thick piece of leather. "Bite on this. It'll help." Then they strapped him to the table.

Glasgow heard an animal whimper. Then the amputated arm fell onto a tubful of amputated arms and legs and slid to the deck.

"Next!"

Sailors picked up another wounded man. The first four heaved the man who'd just been operated on from the table.

Two more sailors stumbled down from the gun deck with a limp body between them. It was Matthews—with one leg dangling.

"A midshipman, sir," one man said. "This leg's got to come off."

The sailors who were lifting a man onto the table stood back.

"Bring him here," the surgeon said to the men who carried Matthews.

Matthews shook his head. "I'll wait my turn," he whispered. The sailors laid him on the deck.

Glasgow knelt by him. "Matthews! It's Farragut! What can I do?"

"Study harder," Matthews whispered. "You're a miserable student. But you're a spunky little . . ." He sighed and was still, but he was still breathing.

"Farragut!" the surgeon said. "Give this man a drink when I'm done with him."

"Aye, aye, sir!"

"Next!"

The sailors bent over Matthews. "He's done for." They picked up another man.

"*Farragut!*"

"Yes, sir!" Numb with shock, he followed orders until the surgeon was done operating. He helped till all the wounded had been taken ashore to a big house and laid on pallets on the floor in a wide hall. Then he went from one man to another, checking to see what he could do.

Once the surgeon put his hand on Glasgow's shoulder. "You're doing all right, Farragut."

"Wasn't there anything I could have done for Matthews?"

106

The surgeon sighed. "We needed tourniquets, and men who knew how to use them."

"Will you show me how to use one, sir?"

"Later," the surgeon said. "We'll have plenty of time here before these men are ready to set sail for home."

"Yes, sir."

Glasgow went back to his work. He saw a man with his hair and beard singed and his face blistered. Glasgow began to shake. He remembered now seeing Kingsbury stumble up from below and plunge over the side of the *Essex*.

First Matthews—then Kingsbury. His good friends. There wasn't a chance that Kingsbury was alive. A man burned that badly wouldn't survive the shock of plunging into the sea. He couldn't possibly make the long swim to shore. Glasgow's throat ached.

The surgeon's mates were greasing the bodies of the burned men and laying cloth over the grease.

"Think you can help?" one asked Glasgow.

He clenched his teeth. "Yes, sir."

After a long time the surgeon said, "That's enough, Farragut. Go get some sleep."

"I'm not sleepy, sir." He didn't want to shut his eyes. He knew what he'd see if he did.

War was a hideous business. Why did men have to fight? Then he thought of all the American sailors who had been seized by the British and forced to serve on their ships—just because America wasn't strong enough to defend her people.

He thought of the shameful business of the Barbary pirates. Captain Porter had told him about that—how America had knuckled under to the Barbary pirates in the Mediterranean and paid tribute to them as the price for letting American merchant ships trade there. That had gone on until America had been strong enough to win a war against them.

Yes, there were things that were worse than war.

He got more grease and more rags and went on about his work. He came to one man almost entirely covered with greasy rags. Only his mouth was exposed.

"Can I get you anything?" Glasgow asked.

"Yes," a voice rumbled. "A long eighteen! And a chance to blow the *Phoebe* to pieces!"

"Kingsbury! I thought you were dead!"

"*Bah*. Take more than that to do me in."

The surgeon stopped by Glasgow. "Get some sleep, Farragut. That's an order."

"Aye, aye, sir!" But when the surgeon had gone, Glasgow muttered, "I'm not going to do it!" He knelt by Kingsbury. "Is there anything I can do for you?"

Kingsbury seemed to be rambling. "Yes. Something. Wanted something bad. Can't think. Stay till I think?"

"Of course!" Glasgow sat down, hugged his knees, and rested his forehead on them. "I'm right here when you think of it!"

Once in a while Kingsbury muttered, but it didn't seem to make sense. Glasgow kept very still so he wouldn't miss anything Kingsbury said.

The next thing he knew the sun was shining, he was lying on the floor by Kingsbury, and the surgeon was smiling down at him.

"Sir!" Glasgow sat up dizzily. "I didn't mean to go to sleep!"

Kingsbury's chuckle rumbled. "Tricked you, didn't I?"

"Captain's compliments, Mr. Farragut," the surgeon said. "You're to report to the *Phoebe*."

"Yes, sir."

Glasgow was in too much of a hurry washing, combing, and brushing to think or feel. Not until he stood in the steerage of the *Phoebe* did he think about what had happened.

The British middies were strutting about, bragging over their victory. For one awful minute Glasgow thought he couldn't keep tears out of his eyes. Then the middies began to tease him:

"Will you look!"

"Someone robbed the nursery!"

"Does your nanny know you're out?"

Another middy came below, carrying Murphy. "A prize! A prize! A fine grunter, by Jove!"

"Yeah, Shorty!" someone yelled.

Glasgow was glad for the anger that burned away the threatened tears. "That's Murphy! He's ours!"

"Oh, ho!" Shorty said. "He's a prize of war! You're our prisoners, and so's your pig!"

"He's private property!" Glasgow yelled. "Or don't you British observe the rules of war?"

"Why, you little . . ." Shorty handed the pig to a sailor. "Hold him while I settle this little wart!"

"If I flatten you," Glasgow asked, "will you give up my pig?"

"If you flatten me? Hah!"

The sailors and middies made a ring around them. Someone yelled, "Go to it, little Yankee! If you can lick Shorty, the pig is yours!"

Shorty was taller and heavier—a lot heavier. But he evidently had not gone through the endless hours of drill in boxing that men got on the *Essex*. Before anyone could quite tell how it happened Shorty was flat on his back, and Glasgow straddled him, fists cocked.

"Had enough?"

Shorty squirmed. Glasgow hit him again.

"Ouch! It's not fair to hit a man when he's down!"

110

"Had enough?"

Shorty mumbled.

"Had enough?"

"Yes!"

"Louder!" Glasgow demanded.

"YES!"

Glasgow jumped up and dodged back, fists cocked just in case Shorty broke the truce.

The sailors cheered. One handed the pig back to Shorty.

"It's his," Shorty mumbled.

An older middy spoke sternly. "Then give it to him!"

Shorty finally smiled. "Here, Yankee. You won him fair and square."

An orderly came to the steerage. "Is there a Mr. Farragut here?"

"I'm Mr. Farragut."

The orderly blinked. "Captain Hillyar's compliments, sir. You will report to his cabin."

Shorty stared and whistled. "Go along, Yankee. I'll take care of Murphy for you. Good care! Honest!"

Glasgow handed over Murphy, brushed at his uniform, smoothed his hair, and followed the orderly.

Captain Porter, looking pale and grim, was having breakfast with Captain Hillyar.

"Sit down, Mr. Farragut," Captain Hillyar said.

"The stewards will serve you."

Glasgow sat. He tried to eat. He could not seem to swallow. All he could do was chew a bite until it seemed to go away.

Captain Hillyar said, "If we disarm the *Essex Junior* and make a cartel ship of her, I believe she can accommodate you and your men?"

"Yes," Captain Porter said with a kind of icy politeness, "I believe so. Of the two-hundred-odd men on the *Essex*, ninety are dead or missing. Of the sixty-odd wounded, some will not survive. Yes, the *Essex Junior* will hold the survivors."

Glasgow jumped to his feet. "Excuse me, sir. But may I report back to the surgeon, sir? He needs me."

Captain Porter eyed him a moment, then spoke curtly. "Go along, Farragut."

Captain Hillyar's tone was kinder. "Don't feel downcast, my little fellow. It may be your turn next."

"I hope so . . . sir!" Glasgow bit out the words, then fled from the cabin. He wasn't going to have anybody—especially not a British captain—see him with tears in his eyes.

Day after day Glasgow worked with the surgeon. He was up by sunrise every morning and worked until breakfast. He never stopped working at night until he was so tired he was numb. He wanted to be numb—too numb to remember.

112

The surgeon showed him how to make and use a tourniquet. He fastened a foot-long stick to a strip of cloth, laid the stick alongside Glasgow's leg, wrapped the cloth around like a bandage, then tightened the bandage by twisting the stick. "It's a last resort," he said. "We only use it to keep a man from bleeding to death."

When I'm captain of my ship, Glasgow thought, every man under me will know how to use a tourniquet! And there'll be plenty of tourniquets too!

Late in April the wounded—all who had survived—were ready for the long voyage home. On Glasgow's thirteenth birthday the *Essex Junior* was nearing New York harbor.

"We ought to celebrate!" Kingsbury said.

"I haven't anything *to* celebrate," Glasgow muttered.

"Lad, you've nothing to be downcast about! You're a credit to your country! The youngest middy ever to command a prize ship! And you fought like a tiger clear through the battle. And you were braver, helping the surgeon, than any man has to be in battle! I'll bet you get a promotion out of this!"

A promotion? Glasgow's heart hammered. He'd been a midshipman before he was ten. Would he be a lieutenant before he was fifteen?

Back in Chester he read about the battle of the

113

Essex in the newspaper. He had been mentioned by name. He had "proved his worth to the navy but was too young to recommend for promotion" Captain Porter had said.

It was in Chester, too, that he found what had happened to the other two ships under Bainbridge; both had fought and defeated British ships but they'd had to return to the United States for repairs.

There was a new baby in the Porter home now —David Dixon Porter, with his father's dark eyes and curly black hair. "A chip off the old block, all right!" the captain said.

Captain Porter was home only a few days. When he said good-bye, he told Glasgow, "As soon as you're exchanged for a British prisoner you'll get orders to report to a ship. Meantime you'll stay here and go to school."

11. "CRACK SHIP"

School! How could anybody expect him to settle down and go to school after what he'd been through in the last three years? But when the captain gave an order, there was only one answer: "Aye, aye, sir."

Fuming, Glasgow marched off to school.

The teacher, Mr. Neif, was a Frenchman who had been one of Napoleon's guards. "Farragut, eh? I hear your father is Spanish?"

"Yes, sir."

"You are lucky—knowing more than one language."

"But I don't, sir."

"What! Why not?"

"My father never talked Spanish around home

115

unless he was—well—excited. He never taught us any."

"What a pity. You, a naval officer, with only one language!"

"What does another language have to do with being in the navy, sir?"

Mr. Neif clutched his head, exploded in French, then asked, "Where do you expect to spend your life? Cruising up and down your own coastline? Putting in at your home ports?"

"Of course not, sir."

"Exactly! American merchants ships sail the seven seas. The navy must sail the seven seas to protect those merchant ships. Young man!" He glared down a bony finger at Glasgow. "Young man! You will represent your country all over the world! Can't you see what it would mean if you could talk to people in their own language?"

"I hadn't thought of that, sir."

"*Bah!* How old are you?"

"Thirteen, sir."

"Thirteen! And you know only one language! *Tsch, tsch!* Well, I'll start you with French. Then we'll go on to Italian, Spanish, and German. In a year or two . . ."

But before long, orders came. Midshipman Farragut had been exchanged. He would sail on the *Spark* when she was ready for action against the British.

Midshipman Farragut! Reporting for duty! He put on his dress uniform and went to school. I have to say good-bye to Mr. Neif, he told himself. But he knew the real reason he was going. He wanted to be there when the other boys heard the news.

The boys shook hands, wished him luck. One even called him "sir."

Mr. Neif said, "A pity. A year or two with me would have dispelled some of your ignorance."

A year or two of school? When his country needed him to fight against the British? Hah! He didn't say what he was thinking.

Soon he was on his way to New York to report to the receiving ship *John Adams*. He had never been on a receiving ship before, but he knew about them. New recruits waited there for assignments; officers waited there to board their ships.

An officer! Waiting to join my ship! That's what I am! Glasgow thought. Confound it, why wasn't the *Spark* ready for action? What if the war ended before the *Spark* was ready to sail?

It did. Glasgow was still on the *John Adams* when the news came. The war was over. He didn't know whether he was glad or sorry. If only he had had just one chance against the British! One chance to wipe out the defeat of the *Essex*!

On the heels of that, other news came. The Bar-

117

bary pirates were making trouble again in the Mediterranean. The United States had declared war. Commodore Bainbridge would command two squadrons in the Mediterranean and settle those Barbary pirates once and for all! One squadron, under Commodore Decatur, would sail from New York. The other, under Commodore Bainbridge, from Boston.

Both officers had fought against the Barbary pirates before. Bainbridge would certainly have a score to settle. The pirates had captured his ship, the *Philadelphia*, and made prisoners of Bainbridge and all his crew.

I wish I'd get to sail with Bainbridge! Glasgow thought. To sail on a ship leading two squadrons —to be on a ship that was going to win a victory!

Days passed while Glasgow waited for orders. Then weeks. He gave up hope. Both squadrons must be halfway to the Mediterranean by now! Finally, six weeks after war was declared, orders came: Midshipman Farragut would report to the *Independence*, Bainbridge's flagship "now being readied for sea in the port of Boston."

"We declare war, and then we get ready!" Glasgow muttered.

It was July, months after war had been declared, before Bainbridge's squadron was ready to sail.

At last the morning came. Glasgow stood on the spar deck of the huge ship with eight hundred officers and men as six side boys at the gangway stood ready to pipe Bainbridge aboard. There must be six to do honor to a commodore.

Commodore Bainbridge appeared, a big man with a rugged face, a thatch of dark hair, and shaggy eyebrows. He frowned as he glanced over the deck, answered salutes, then strode aft to his cabin on the poop deck.

Captain Crane, a slim, quiet man, followed the commodore aboard. His smile flashed as he answered salutes. He paused to speak to several of his officers. Then, with another smile that seemed to take in the whole crew, he went below.

How good it made a man feel when his captain smiled that way! When I'm a captain, Glasgow told himself, I'm going to remember this!

As soon as they were under way an orderly came to Glasgow. Midshipman Farragut would report to the captain's cabin.

As often as Glasgow had heard that message he still wondered for a moment if something was wrong. Weren't all his buttons shined? He checked, then went below.

Captain Crane greeted him with a smile. "At ease, Mr. Farragut. I want you for captain's aide."

"Thank you, sir."

"Your father is George Farragut, isn't he?"

"Yes, sir."

"I've heard of his service in the Revolutionary War. A proud record."

"Thank you, sir." With a warm feeling running through his veins, Glasgow left the cabin.

All the way across the Atlantic he was in and out of the captain's cabin. Often Commodore Bainbridge was there. Once Glasgow heard him say, "It's going to be a sweet revenge!"

When the squadron reached the Mediterranean, Glasgow could feel the excitement running through the crew. Soon they would meet the Dey of Algiers and make him knuckle under!

A ship of the United States Navy came alongside, saluted, and gave them the news. The war was over. Commodore Decatur had conquered the Dey of Algiers.

The war was over! Cheers echoed over the ship. Glasgow happened to glance at Commodore Bainbridge. His face was white, his jaw set, his eyes blazing. He was furious.

And after the first cheers, a strange mood settled over the ship. Men who had been alert began to slump; men who had been friendly began to fight. On the voyage home there were more floggings in one week than there had been in the whole crossing from Boston. Glasgow could not understand.

The United States had won the war. Didn't victory please a navy man?

Commodore Bainbridge ordered the squadron exercised at sailing in formation. Glasgow spent every waking minute on deck. His gaze never left the sight of the ships. Even when he shut his eyes, he could still see them, proud ships—dark hulls rising from the sea, the water curling back from their prows, and the cloud of white sails above. Nothing was so beautiful as a ship in full sail. He hoped he would spend three-fourths of his life at sea. Maybe even nine-tenths of it.

One day Captain Crane said, "I believe you have a brother in the navy?"

"Yes, sir. William. He's older than I am. He's with the Naval Station in New Orleans."

"Do you have any other brothers?"

"One, sir. George. He's at home with my father."

"Do you think your father would like for him to get an appointment as a midshipman?"

"More than anything, sir. But George is just a little fellow."

"How old?"

Glasgow counted up. "Why, he's ten, sir! Older than I was when I joined the navy. Funny. I keep thinking of him as just a little fellow."

The captain smiled. "I know. We navy men

have to get used to that. Realizing that the world does not stand still when we're away. Well, we'll see if we can't do something for young George."

"Thank you, sir!"

That night before he turned in, Glasgow wrote to his father about it. "I haven't gotten ahead very fast," he told his father. "I'm still just a midshipman. Maybe George will be the one to make you so proud you'll bust the buttons off your coat."

When the *Independence* reached port, mail waited. There was even a letter for Midshipman Farragut. He saw the handwriting and smiled. Dear Nancy! She always kept in touch. He opened the letter, took one look, then swallowed hard. His brother George was dead. He had drowned.

"You remember how Father seemed to get old after Mother died?" Nancy wrote. "It's worse now. Like he didn't have anything to live for. I wish you could get home to see him."

But new orders came. Midshipman Farragut would report to the *Washington*, now being readied for a tour of duty in the Mediterranean.

"The *Washington*, eh?" an officer said.

"Yes, sir!" Glasgow smiled. "Another of the big ones. A seventy-four!"

"She'll be 'the crack ship of the navy,'" the officer said. "Creighton is to command her. His first command as a captain. I served under him when

he was an executive officer. He's a martinet—*the*
martinet of the navy. I hope you never get on the
down-wind side of his temper." Then he added
thoughtfully, "No, it isn't exactly temper. It's
worse than that. He's mean without being mad.
My sympathy, Farragut."

Glasgow didn't worry about the warning. Any
naval officer was something of a martinet, wasn't
he? He went aboard the *Washington* and looked
around with satisfaction. He was used to naval
ships being shipshape. But there was something
special about the *Washington*. No doubt about it!
Even before the captain was aboard, she was be-
coming the "crack ship of the navy."

He saluted the quarter-deck, saluted the O.D.,
and went to report to the First.

The First looked him over coldly. Glasgow had
a feeling that if there had been a speck of dust on
the back of his coat, the First could have seen it.

"You may find quarters in the steerage."

That was all. No welcome, no pleasant words.
But, after all, he didn't have to be patted on the
head, did he? He saluted, left the cabin, and went
forward to the steerage. Two middies were standing there looking lost. Glasgow remembered his
first days on the *Essex* and how kind Matthews
had been.

"Hello there! I'm Glasgow Farragut."

One boy was fair, big-eyed, and solemn. He

gulped. "I'm Dan Scott." He nodded toward the other boy, a wiry little fellow with a thatch of red hair, freckles, and a grin. "He's Peter Miller."

Young Miller wasn't scared. "Hi!" His grin spread. "Or should I say 'Ahoy' or something like that?"

Glasgow laughed with them, showed them where to stow their gear and swing their hammocks. He took them over the ship and explained things to them. They didn't know as much about a ship as he had known when he was ten.

When they got back to the steerage, another middy was there—an older one, six feet tall, sandy haired, with cold blue eyes and a one-sided curl to his mouth. He reminded Glasgow of Channing.

The middy whipped a glance over the new boys, ignored them, and turned to Glasgow. "I'm Warner. Who are you?"

"Farragut."

Warner's eyes widened. "Farragut? The one that was on the *Essex*? I heard about that." His voice was almost respectful. Then his lip curled. "Have you seen the teacher for the *Washington*? Youngest one I've ever seen on a ship. Will we lead him a life!"

The middies gathered next morning for their first class. A young man—he did look very young —entered briskly.

"I'm Charles Folsom," he said. "As I call your

124

names I want each of you to tell me how far along you are in mathematics—how much algebra you've had—geometry—trigonometry—and so forth."

When roll call was over, Glasgow's face was burning. Even Miller and Scott knew more mathematics than he did.

Mr. Folsom looked at him thoughtfully. "Where have you had your schooling, Mr. Farragut?"

"Mostly on shipboard, sir. I reported to my first tour of duty when I was ten."

Mr. Folsom nodded. "That accounts for it." He smiled. "I know how it is on shipboard. 'All hands on deck!' and lessons stop."

Glasgow's face still burned, but he relaxed. At least Mr. Folsom understood.

"Well," Mr. Folsom said, "we'll do our best to remedy the situation—the bosun's pipe permitting."

An appreciative chuckle ran through the class. Warner was sitting with his arms crossed and his lips curled, but Glasgow knew he was not going to get very far trying to make trouble for this teacher.

"Your slates and pencils, gentlemen." Mr. Folsom scanned the roll. Then without referring to a book, he dictated a problem to each middy. As the boys began to work he strolled around to see how they were getting along.

One boy looked up, shamefaced. Yes, he had

had that, but he didn't seem to remember how to do it right now.

"Then we'll back up a bit and catch up on what you've missed. Mathematics is like mountain climbing. One handhold, one foothold after another. If you miss one, you're apt to take a tumble."

For the first time in his life Glasgow wanted to knuckle down and study. He was going to stand at the top of the class or he'd die trying!

But no matter how much he learned, the others still outdistanced him. He might know more of practical things—the rigging of a ship backwards and forwards—all the orders for maneuvers—but as a student he floundered along in the wake of the others. And "a stern chase is a long chase." Grimly, he remembered that.

The morning came to sail. Six side boys piped Commodore Chauncey aboard. Captain Creighton followed—hatchet-faced and stern. Cold gray eyes scanned the officers, the marines, the sailors. He returned their salute, said something to the First, and went below. Glasgow could feel a chill settle over the deck.

The First said, "Farragut, you are to be captain's aide. You will report to his cabin."

"Aye, aye, sir. Before we get under way or after?"

The First spoke with deadly quiet. "When you

are ordered to report to Captain Creighton, there is no delay. Ever."

"Aye, aye, sir."

Captain Creighton's reception was chillier than the First's had been. The cold gray stare went over Glasgow inch by inch. "You will report when we are under way." Nothing else.

"Aye, aye, sir." In spite of telling himself that "all naval officers are martinets," Glasgow had a lump in the pit of his stomach.

After three weeks on the *Washington* he was heartsick and furious by turns. Captain Creighton and his First seemed to take a savage delight in browbeating the men. In all his years at sea Glasgow had never heard that cry so many times: "All hands to witness punishment ahoy!"

A man might break a rule, or perhaps only blunder. Not only that man but every man on the watch might be spread-eagled for a dozen of the cat. Another time, both watches might be kept on deck night and day for twelve watches. Another time they might get no food after a cold breakfast until breakfast the next day.

With God's help, Glasgow swore to himself, I'll never run a "crack ship" at the price of breaking men's spirits!

Not only the sailors but also the middies and

127

lesser lieutenants seethed under Creighton's rule. The only bright spot in his life on the *Washington*, Glasgow decided, was school. He smiled to himself over that. To imagine he'd ever think school was the bright spot of a day!

The *Washington* was on station in the Mediterranean when Warner swaggered to the steerage one day and said in a tone that promised trouble, "Folsom wants to see you, Farragut. In his cabin. On the double."

Glasgow's heart skipped a beat, then hurried to make up for lost time. He knew Mr. Folsom must be disappointed in him. What was the teacher going to say? Shivering inside, he went aft to Mr. Folsom's cabin.

"Come in, Farragut! Sit down!" Mr. Folsom was smiling.

At least he was not utterly disgusted. Glasgow felt better.

"Farragut, you seem to have—well—waked up to what school is all about."

"Yes, sir. Finally! All my life I've—well—"

"You've been more interested in the practical side of the navy?"

"Yes, sir. I'm afraid so."

"I don't know if you've heard about the new system of promoting a midshipman to lieutenant. He must go before a Board of Examiners. The

Board will question him on seamanship, mathematics, and all the other things he is supposed to have learned. If he passes that examination, he'll be a Passed Midshipman. Not a lieutenant yet. Just a Passed Midshipman, eligible for promotion to lieutenant. Had you heard of that?"

"No, sir. I guess I'd better dig in harder than ever. I hope you'll be with the *Washington* as long as I am, sir."

Mr. Folsom shook his head. "No, I'm leaving the *Washington* very soon. Our Consul in Tunis is going home. I have been offered the post in his place. It's rather a feather in my cap—to be a consul before I'm twenty-five."

Glasgow wanted to shout, No! You can't do that! You can't leave the *Washington*! But he said, "Congratulations, sir. I'm happy for you." Even as he said it he heard how glum it sounded. "I really am happy for you, sir. Just not for me."

"Would you like a leave of absence to go to Tunis with me and study for six months?"

"Mr. Folsom!"

"That means you would? Fine. You have Commodore Chauncey's permission. I just wanted to know how you'd feel about a chance for serious study."

"You'll find out how I feel about it, sir! You'll see me making up for lost time!"

129

12. SUNSTROKE

Just after Christmas of 1817, Glasgow and Mr. Folsom were in Tunis. Glasgow settled down to study French, Italian, mathematics, and English literature. Often he stopped, shook his head, and groaned, "The things I don't know!"

"You're making up for lost time," Mr. Folsom always said. "So go to it, Farragut!" But after two months he was saying, "My dear Farragut, you don't have to learn everything in one week!"

"I have only this one chance to make up for lost time." And Glasgow studied harder than ever.

He had a knack with languages. Soon he could speak Italian and French with people in the other consulates. He was picking up quite a bit of Arabic too. But mathematics and English literature—they weren't so easy.

130

After three months he paid for overwork with a headache that would not go away.

"Enough is enough!" Mr. Folsom said. When some people of the other consulates were going on a sightseeing trip, he insisted that he and Glasgow go along. A rest would be a good idea.

The desert was hot—brutally hot. One day Glasgow was dizzy with the heat. He started to say something about it. The next thing he knew he was lying on a pallet and someone was putting cold packs on his head.

He tried to say "What's the matter?" But his tongue was stiff and the words were a jumble.

The man bending over him said, "Don't worry. It's just sunstroke."

Sunstroke! Glasgow remembered, years ago, seeing men bring old Captain Porter to the house. He remembered their faces when they looked at him, shook their heads, and went away. The captain had died.

"I won't die!" he shouted. "I won't! I've got things to do!" The words were a jumble.

The man said, "Don't worry. You'll get over it. You're young and strong."

By the time Glasgow got back to Tunis the sunstroke was almost forgotten. The stiffness had gone out of his tongue. It was not until he started to study again that he discovered the trouble with his eyes. Before he had read for ten minutes the words started to blur.

Mr. Folsom sent for the best doctor in Tunis. He came. He questioned Glasgow. He examined his eyes. He clucked his tongue. "What is your profession?"

"The navy, sir."

"A man of action, eh? That is good. I'm afraid, my young friend, that you may not have a chance to be a scholar."

"You mean—I'll always have trouble with my eyes?"

The doctor shrugged and spread his hands. "We cannot say. Maybe yes. Maybe no. The chances are—maybe yes."

When the doctor had gone, Glasgow sat with his head in his hands, not saying anything. Mr. Folsom didn't say anything either. He left the room.

Presently Mr. Folsom came back.

Glasgow said, "I've wasted my time. Now it's too late."

"None of that!" Mr. Folsom spoke sharply. "Don't waste time in useless regrets." Then he went on more quietly. "I've written to Commodore Chauncey asking that your leave be extended another six months. I'm sure he'll grant it. Meantime I'll read to you. You'll be amazed at how much you can get through your ears when you put your mind to it."

"Thank you. And I didn't mean to whine."

"I'd hope not!" Mr. Folsom was stern again. Then he smiled. "Besides, the doctor may be wrong. You may recover from this very soon."

But Glasgow did not. A page at a time was all he could read; then the type began to blur. Once he slammed a book shut and hammered it with his fist.

"That's enough of that!" Mr. Folsom snapped. "Come on, now. Shut your eyes and *listen*."

At first it was slow work trying to remember what he heard. After a time it went better. The answer came from Commodore Chauncey. Midshipman Farragut's leave was extended.

A whole year to study! Even if he did have to get it through his ears, he was getting a lot.

In September they heard rumors that the plague had struck Tunis. At first only rumors. Then facts. Thirty deaths a day. By October the death toll had mounted to one hundred deaths a day.

One morning Mr. Folsom said, "The Danish consul is leaving Tunis Thursday. You are going with him."

"But, sir—"

"And that's final!"

So the last months of his precious year of study

were lopped off. Glasgow returned to his squadron and was assigned to the *Franklin* under Captain Gallagher.

At first he tried to cover up the trouble with his eyes. Any time he saw a younger middy scowling over a lesson, he'd sit down by him, shut his eyes and say, "Read me what's bothering you. Let's see if we can figure it out."

Word spread that Farragut was the squarest, fairest, kindest midshipman on the *Franklin*.

He did not know when the boys caught on that he was having trouble with his eyes. But one day Captain Gallagher sent for him.

"What's this about trouble with your eyes, Farragut?"

Glasgow explained.

"Why have you tried to hide it?"

Glasgow started to lie, then admitted, "I hoped it would go away. If it didn't, I hoped I could cover up. I was afraid the navy would dismiss me."

"I see no reason for that," the captain said. "Your vision is all right on long distances, isn't it?"

"Yes, sir."

"Then I see no reason to think of dismissal. Of course if the trouble got much worse—but let's not cross that bridge until we come to it, eh?"

"Thank you, sir!"

In spite of the captain's assurances Glasgow had a sinking feeling every time he was summoned to the captain's cabin.

Then he got orders that had him walking on air. Midshipman Farragut was to be acting lieutenant, executive officer, second in command, on the brig *Spark*.

"The *Spark* . . . *hmmmm*." An older middy looked thoughtful. "Well, you'll get plenty of practice commanding a ship. In fact, you'll be in full charge most of the time."

"Why?"

"Haven't you heard about 'Bottles'? That's what we call the captain of the *Spark*—behind his back. You will too. Just don't let him hear you say it. Don't let him hear you say anything but 'Yes, sir; no, sir; aye, aye, sir; right away, sir!' "

Most days on the *Spark* started the same way. Bottles might appear on deck about five bells of the forenoon watch, with bloodshot eyes and a hangover. "If you need me, don't hesitate to call me."

"Aye, aye, sir!"

And Bottles would disappear into his cabin. Glasgow soon learned it was useless to try to rouse him by the dogwatch.

So Acting-Lieutenant Farragut learned to sleep

135

with one eye open, to be awake and alert in an instant. He would appear topside at any hour, day or night. He liked to be on deck, no matter what the time: early morning during the hustle and bustle of cleaning or in the middle of the night when only the tread of the officer on watch, the cries of the watchman, and the *bong* of the ship's bell broke the stillness. Yes, this was his life!

One night he found a young middy leaning against a gun, asleep at his post.

Glasgow put his hand over the lad's mouth so he wouldn't cry out, then whispered. "*Shhh!* Wake up, mister!" When the heavy eyelids opened, he released the boy and stepped back.

The middy looked at him in terror. "Oh, sir!"

"*Shhh!* At ease." Glasgow leaned close. "I'll tell you a secret. I did that once myself when I was very young. And do you know what happened? A kind officer covered me with his jacket so I wouldn't get cold. I swore that someday I'd do the same for another middy—forgive him one nap—just one."

"I'll never do it again, sir!"

"I know. It never happened to me again either."

As the days passed, his patience in training the crew paid off. They were on their toes, alert, and determined to be "the smartest ship in the squadron." He finally overheard their nickname for

136

him: the "Little Luff." Luff was slang for lieutenant. He was only acting lieutenant, but to his men
he was the Little Luff.

He was still on the *Spark* when a letter from
Nancy caught up with him. Their father had died.
Glasgow stuffed the letter in his sleeve and went
to his cabin to read it. "He never got over George's
death," Nancy said. "He was so old and pitiful it
broke your heart. But he was awfully proud of
you—about what was in the paper about the
cruise of the *Essex*. He cut that out and carried it
with him. He told everybody about 'his son that
had sailed with Porter on the *Essex*.' So you did
make him proud."

The ship lurched in a sudden storm. Voices
bawled, "All hands on deck to reef sails!"

For twenty-four hours Glasgow fought the wind
and raging seas. He was glad he was too busy to
think or feel.

The summer of 1820 he got new orders. Midshipman Farragut would report home to take his
examinations to qualify as Passed Midshipman.

"You'll have no trouble there," an officer told
him. "You're probably the most experienced midshipman in the navy!"

Late in September Glasgow was in Washington.
He wrote to the Secretary of the Navy, reporting

himself ready for his examinations, then he went to visit Captain Porter—now Commodore Porter, one of the Board of Navy Commissioners.

"Wait till you see our new home, Glasgow!" the commodore said.

Glasgow's first glimpse had his eyes popping. With the proceeds from prize ships the commodore had bought over a hundred acres on a ridge overlooking Washington. Since the land was on the meridian of Washington, he called his estate Meridian Hill.

Meridian Hill was more than a home: It was almost a village with orchards, gardens, stables, and cottages for workmen. There were dozens of servants, indoors and out, and whole families that worked in the fields.

There were five children in the Porter home now; the second boy, David Dixon, looked more like his father every day. Seven in the family—but generally twice that many sat down to dinner. Every important person, from the United States or abroad, who came to Washington came to Meridian Hill.

He's living like an English lord, Glasgow thought, but I wonder if he misses the sea? I know I would!

Glasgow had not seen half of Meridian Hill when his orders came. The Board of Examiners was sitting in New York. Midshipman Farragut

138

would go to New York and hold himself in readiness to appear before them.

"Come back when examinations are over," the commodore said, "and we'll splice the main brace to celebrate."

"I hope I'll have something to celebrate, sir."

"What? You're not worried about those examinations, are you? Bah! There isn't a midshipman in the navy with half your experience."

"I wish I knew more mathematics."

"Nonsense. You'll do all right. Come back when it's over. That's an order."

"Aye, aye, sir."

He hurried to New York, reported his address to the Board, then settled down to wait—and study while he waited. Luckily he found another midshipman, John Hardy, waiting too. They studied together. Hardy read and Glasgow listened.

"How do you remember things that way?" Hardy asked.

"Because I have to."

"Say, Farragut, did you hear the scuttlebutt about Bottles? He's been ordered home to face a charge of drunkenness on duty."

"No wonder," Glasgow said. "But I have a lot to thank Bottles for. I got a lot of experience on the *Spark* because of him. Even in emergencies I generally had to depend on myself."

That afternoon Glasgow got a letter. "It must be

official," he said. "Nobody but the Board knows where I am." He read it, snorted, wadded it into a ball, and started writing an answer.

"What's the joke?" Hardy asked.

"It's from a friend of Bottles. Full of dark remarks about 'officers who spread rumors about fellow officers.' And ordering me to come to see him."

"What are you going to do?"

"I'm telling him if he wants to see me he knows where I am."

"What's his rank?"

"Captain."

"*Whew!* And you're defying him?"

"He has no right to order me around. I'm not serving under him." He finished the letter, scrawled his signature, and said, "There! That's that!"

Two afternoons later Hardy and Glasgow went out to walk to "clear the cobwebs out of their heads." As they crossed a street they noticed that two men—both naval captains—were waiting to confront them. The one was short and pompous, the other tall and hatchet-faced. Both were staring at Glasgow.

Hardy and Glasgow saluted.

The pompous little captain flushed with anger. "Midshipman Farragut, I ordered you to report to me. You refused. I have things to say to you!"

140

"As a captain, or as a friend of the one-time captain of the *Spark*, sir?" Glasgow asked.

"As a captain!"

"Then, sir, I have nothing to say to you." Glasgow saluted again, passed the captains, and strode on.

"*Whew!*" Hardy said. "Heaven help you if you ever serve under him!"

"The point is I'm not serving under him. Anyhow I think his bark would be worse than his bite. That other one—that hatchet-face—he'd be meaner. He made me think of Captain Creighton. Did you ever serve under him?"

"No, but I've heard of him."

"He was so mean he made me sick at my stomach. Well, that's that. Let's get back to work."

Three days later Glasgow went for his examinations, entered the room, and stopped short. His heart sank. There sat Hatchet-Face staring at him coldly.

Blood pounded in Glasgow's ears until he did not hear the first question Hatchet-Face asked. He had to say, "Will you please repeat the question, sir?"

Hatchet-Face roared the question. It was on mathematics, where Glasgow felt most unsure of himself. But he managed to answer correctly.

All the officers seemed to sense his uncertainty.

They hammered him with questions on mathematics. To his relief he answered all of them correctly.

They switched to questions on handling a ship. Glasgow relaxed: They couldn't stump him there!

Suddenly Hatchet-Face interrupted. "No, no! We cannot let an error like that pass. When you lowered your topmasts you did not clear away your bowlines."

"But, sir, I did!"

Hatchet-Face froze. "Are you calling me a liar?"

"No, sir. You must not have heard me. But, sir, I have given that order hundreds of times. When I was executive officer on the *Spark*—" He stopped. Why, oh why, had he mentioned the *Spark*? He turned to the other officers. "You gentlemen heard me clear away my bowlines, didn't you?"

They did not look at him. They looked at one another and then at Hatchet-Face. If their fellow officer had not heard it, then undoubtedly Mr. Farragut had not answered correctly, one said.

"But, gentlemen—"

It was too late. With a tight little smile, Hatchet-Face was stacking his papers together. The examination was over. Heartsick, Glasgow stood, bowed, and left the room.

The results were posted: Midshipman Farragut had failed. "Adequate in mathematics; deficient in other respects."

142

13. SUSAN

He had promised to go to Meridian Hill after his examinations. It was the last thing Glasgow wanted to do, but he went.

The minute he got there he knew Commodore Porter had heard about his failure. The commodore led the way to his library and closed the door.

"What happened?"

Glasgow told him about the dust-up over Bottles, and Hatchet-Face. Then he flared. "But I'll not take this standing still! I'm going to the Secretary of the Navy! I'll demand they tell me in what way I was 'deficient in other respects'! And I'll demand I take the examination again under another board!"

"The Secretary of the Navy couldn't order that, Glasgow. It would be an insult to your Board of Examiners. No, you'll just have to live with it. Of course," he added dryly, "you'll always have the satisfaction of knowing that you had the last word with a superior officer. Yes, sir! Mr. Farragut, midshipman, defied a captain!"

For the first time Glasgow saw himself for what he had been—an arrogant, stiff-necked young fool.

"I remember a saying of Franklin's," the commodore went on. " 'Better to bow your head a little than to bump it against a beam.' "

Glasgow had no answer.

The commodore sighed. "I'm sorry, Glasgow. You're going to pay for this the rest of your life. It will always be on your record that you failed your examinations once." Then he shrugged, smiled, and said, "Well, that's enough of that. The only thing is to forget it."

But Glasgow could not forget. All the jolly hospitality of Meridian Hill could not cheer him up. He'd go to Norfolk. He knew the Dixons, relatives of Mrs. Porter, were there. He knew he'd be welcome. Norfolk would be better. . . .

But Norfolk was not better. The Dixons greeted him warmly. But he felt they were talking very fast to cover up what they were thinking, Poor fellow, he failed his examinations.

One day Lieutenant Williams, a friend of his, asked him to a dance.

"Why?" Glasgow asked. "To cheer me up?" Then he flushed. "I'm sorry. I'll be glad to come. I'll dance every dance and I won't forget to smile."

"Good!"

The dance was the hardest experience yet. Everybody was very evidently thinking about his failure and talking brightly about something else.

Presently the lieutenant said, "Mr. Farragut, I want you to meet my little cousin, Susan Marchant. She's an imp, but I love her."

Glasgow smiled at a tumble of brown curls and dancing blue eyes. She wasn't more than sixteen— if that old. He bowed low over her hand. "Miss Marchant. I'm honored."

Susan answered with an impish curtsy and touched the tip of a finger to her chin. "Mr. Farragut! Farragut . . . oh, yes! You're the one that everybody is—is—*tiptoeing* about, aren't you?"

"Susan!" her cousin gasped.

"I mean," she went on, "because you failed your examinations. Nobody will talk about it so of course nobody can think of anything else. That's what I mean—*tiptoeing*."

Glasgow smiled. "Susan Marchant, you're delightful!"

"Do you want me to make them stop tiptoeing?"

145

"How?"

"Listen!" When the music stopped, she made a megaphone of her hands and sang out, "Now hear this! Now hear this!"

Silence. Everybody turned to look at her.

"Now hear this! We all know Midshipman Farragut failed his examinations. So let's stop *tiptoeing* about it!"

A shocked silence, then everybody laughed and clapped. For the first time since that grim day in New York, Glasgow had hopes he'd get over the way he'd been feeling.

The music started again. He bowed over Susan's hand. As they began to dance she looked up quickly. "Cousin John said you were a good dancer, but you're wonderful. Where did you learn?"

"In the navy. Anything I know I've had to learn in the navy. I joined before I was ten."

"I've always wondered how navy men keep their words sorted out. You know—land talk and sea talk. On land we talk English. At sea—goodness knows what you talk!"

"We have a few special terms, but it's not really that bad."

When the music stopped she said, "You don't have anything *but* special words. Perfectly good words mean the craziest things on a ship. On land,

146

sheets are things you put on a bed. At sea, sheets are ropes. On land, chains are necklaces or something like that. At sea, chains are shelves that stick out on the side of a ship. On land . . . What are you laughing about?"

Glasgow realized he was laughing. He had been wondering if he'd ever laugh again. Bless her!

When the dance ended, Glasgow beamed at Mr. Williams. "Thank you for asking me! I don't know when I've had more fun!"

"Don't thank me. Thank Susan."

"I'm going to stay in Norfolk a while," Glasgow said. "At least till I get orders."

"Shall I let Susan know?"

"Fine. You know, she makes me think of my little sisters. I haven't had a chance to see them for years."

Mr. Williams looked solemn. He nodded. "I see. I'll tell Susan that you feel like a big brother to her."

Not long after, Glasgow met Susan on the street.

"Oh, Mr. Farragut, I've heard you're staying in Norfolk for a while and that you want me for a little sister. I think that's wonderful. Are you going to study for your examinations? I'd like to help you. You know—to see if a navy man ever does talk English."

"That will be grand!'"

147

He spent a great deal of time in Susan's home. "Mr. Farragut" became "Glasgow."

Once Mrs. Marchant said, "I declare, I never knew studying was amusing. You and Susan laugh more than you work."

Susan had caught on very quickly to the trouble he had reading. After that, she read, he listened, explained—and laughed.

One evening when he returned to Dixon's, his orders waited. Where was he going? He'd have to tell Susan . . . Odd how he felt about telling Susan he was going away. He opened the letter. Mr. Farragut would report to the Commandant of the Norfolk Navy Yard for duty.

Susan sparkled at the news. "Oh, that's grand! I *like* having you for a big brother!"

In October new orders: Midshipman Farragut would report to New York to the Board of Examiners.

"You'll pass this time!" Susan said. "And I'll feel so important. Because I helped you study."

I'll pass, Glasgow thought, if Hatchet-Face isn't on the Board. And I'll stand at the top! That'll give the Navy Department something to think about! How could a man fail one year and stand at the top the next year?

Hatchet-Face wasn't on the Board. Glasgow passed, but he didn't stand at the top. He was number twenty-two on a list of fifty-three. Nothing about that record to give the Navy Department something to think about. Passed-Midshipman Farragut was just average. That was all.

He wrote asking for sea duty, then went back to Norfolk to wait for orders.

Susan glowed at the news. "Oh, Glasgow!" She stood on tiptoe and kissed his cheek. "That's because I'm so proud of you! And I think *I* deserve one, too, for helping!"

Just as Glasgow bent to kiss Susan, Mrs. Marchant spoke from the doorway. "Glasgow Farragut!"

What could he say?

"Don't blame him, Mother!" Susan said. "I started it."

"Susan! You—you—" Her mother smiled and shook her head. "I never *knew* such a girl."

"You mean because I say what I think? I don't fib and pretend? But I *like* Glasgow. I think maybe I almost *love* him."

Her mother was really shocked. "Susan! Young ladies do not say such things! Glasgow, I think you'd better go."

"Yes, Mrs. Marchant. Good-bye for now, Susan."

He was glad to escape. He had some thinking to do. How long before he'd be a lieutenant and have the right to say what he'd like to say to Susan? Now he was only Passed-Midshipman Farragut with a pretty sorry record. All his experience at sea could not wipe out that record: failed his examinations once, stood number twenty-two the second time. If only he could get sea duty again! He'd show them!

Orders came. Midshipman Farragut would report to the *John Adams*, now being readied for service in the Gulf of Mexico. He smiled wryly at that. Glasgow Farragut—who had doubled Cape Horn and served in the South Pacific, who had crossed the Atlantic four times, who had served in the Mediterranean on the biggest ships of the navy—Glasgow Farragut would serve on the *John Adams*, which was not half as big as the *Essex*, for a tour of duty in the Gulf of Mexico. Like dabbling in a pond, he thought, after sailing on a huge lake. He could do this tour of duty with his eyes shut. But at least it was sea duty.

The *John Adams* had a special mission Captain Renshaw told him. The Mexicans had rebelled against Spain and declared their freedom. In the confusion that followed the revolution, Americans in Mexico—"Anglos" the Mexicans called them—had been imprisoned and their money confiscated. The *John Adams* was to carry the U.S. Minister to Mexico to land him at Vera Cruz, and then stand

150

by to pick him up at another port and help in any way possible. What delighted Glasgow was the name of the minister to Mexico. It was Mr. Poinsett, whom Glasgow had met years ago in Chile.

When the *John Adams* piped Minister Poinsett aboard, Glasgow stood on deck, smothering a grin that wanted to spread from ear to ear and wondering if Mr. Poinsett would remember him.

"Well, Mr. Farragut!" Minister Poinsett said, "We meet again!" He turned to the captain. "I'll never forget meeting Mr. Farragut the summer of 1813 in Valparaiso. He was in command of a prize ship—the youngest navy man ever to have a command."

Glasgow did not know whether it was because of the minister's words or not, but Captain Renshaw gave him special duty. When they anchored off Vera Cruz, the captain chose Midshipman Farragut to go ashore with him and Minister Poinsett. They met the young Mexican general, Santa Anna —"The Napoleon of the West" men called him.

Santa Anna—slim, dark, and handsome—talked with great enthusiasm about Iturbide, their emperor, and about freedom and justice for his people. Glasgow listened as Santa Anna talked and Mr. Poinsett translated. He thought again of how Mr. Neif had scolded him for not knowing Spanish.

He told Mr. Poinsett about it.

"The first two words you'll learn in Spanish," Mr. Poinsett said, "are *mañana* and *pronto*." He smiled. "You say *pronto*—quickly—and they'll say *mañana*—tomorrow."

They set the date for picking up Minister Poinsett at Tampico, promised him the *John Adams* would be standing by, and left him at Vera Cruz.

When the time came for them to meet Mr. Poinsett in Tampico, the *John Adams* was becalmed in a sea as smooth as glass. Captain Renshaw paced the deck impatiently. "Sometimes," he said, "I have to admire Fulton and his steamboats. Just for river traffic, of course. You couldn't have ocean-going vessels with nothing but a steam engine. But right now it would be good to have an auxiliary engine so we could put in at Tampico."

An American schooner was becalmed near the *John Adams*.

"Mr. Farragut," the captain said, "take a boat to the schooner, my compliments to the master, and invite him over. We might as well enjoy a visit with him. Nobody is going anywhere for a while."

Glasgow brought the grizzled old master to the *John Adams*. Just as the old fellow came aboard, a slight breeze stirred from the north.

"A norther!" the old man said. "I've got to get back to my ship!" He grabbed a trumpet from the

152

O.D. and bellowed toward his schooner. "A norther!" He spoke to Captain Renshaw. "Reef sails! Right down to bare poles!" As Glasgow took him back to his schooner the old man bellowed through his cupped hands. "A norther!"

Silly to get in a stew about such a little breeze, Glasgow thought. He had barely got back to the *John Adams* when the storm broke. He stared, dumbfounded. If the old master of the schooner had not warned them, the *John Adams* could have been overset before they reefed a sail. And I thought duty in the Gulf of Mexico would be tame!

The gale ended as abruptly as it began. Once more the *John Adams* was becalmed. The sun beat down. On deck the seams oozed tar. The next two days the *John Adams* worked her way by fits and starts, as little breezes stirred or died.

They got close enough for a boat to reach shore. "I'm sending you to Tampico to meet the minister," Captain Renshaw told Glasgow. "Get there as soon as you can. We're late now."

"Aye, aye, sir!" Glasgow wore the lightest-weight clothes he had except for the coat and hat of his dress uniform. One had to uphold the dignity of the navy. With Spanish doubloons to cover expenses and his dirk to take care of any emergency, he went ashore.

On the beach an old man came to meet him.

"How far to Tampico?" Glasgow asked.

"Three leagues, *señor*."

"I'll need a horse and a guide, please."

"*Mañana?*"

"*Pronto!*"

The old man shrugged. "You need a horse, yes; a guide, no. Just follow the beach, *señor*." He brought a sturdy-looking horse named Blanco.

Glasgow paid for the horse, mounted, and rode off. As soon as he was out of sight of the old man he took off his coat. An hour later another norther howled down—a wet norther this time. He put on his coat and wished for something heavier—even a tarpaulin. Shivering, his teeth chattering, he slogged on. At last in the falling darkness a light glimmered ahead. He dug in his heels to urge Blanco on. But the noble beast seemed to have just two speeds—slow and slower. He slogged ahead, then stopped dead. They had come to the bank of a river. The lights Glasgow had seen were across the river. Nothing he could do would persuade Blanco to swim across.

He yelled himself hoarse trying to rouse someone on the other side. He had almost given up when he heard the splash of oars and someone called, "You need help, *señor*?"

"I must get to Tampico!"

"*Mañana?*"

"*Pronto!*"

The men told him to turn his horse loose; Blanco would find his way home. They'd take him across the river, but he could never find his way to Tampico at night. Maybe *mañana?*

"Tonight! *Pronto!*"

They'd see if anybody was fool enough to be his guide tonight. Surely *mañana* . . .

It was after midnight when Glasgow, drenched, cold, and hungry, reached Tampico. The next morning he went to find Minister Poinsett.

The minister hadn't come yet. Maybe *mañana* . . .

Glasgow leaned against a wall and laughed.

The Mexicans beamed. They liked a cheerful man, they said. Most Anglos were too impatient. Everything *pronto*!

It was over two weeks before Minister Poinsett arrived. Glasgow was having a fine time learning Spanish.

When I get back to Norfolk, he thought, I must tell Susan . . ."

But when the *John Adams* reached home, a message waited. Midshipman Farragut would report to Commodore Porter in Washington immediately.

What in the world?

14. UNDECLARED WAR

Commodore Porter's first words were "Would you like to serve with me in the West Indies?"

So the commodore wanted the sea again! "Fine, sir!"

"It's going to be hot, dangerous, dirty fighting, but—"

"You mean there's going to be war?"

"There *is* war! An undeclared war against the pirates of the West Indies! Heaven knows how many of our merchant ships they've captured, seized the cargo, murdered the crew, and burned the ship. We've been fighting that war for three years."

"And we can't lick them?"

"The ships we've had down there are too deep-draft. Can't follow the pirates into their hideouts.

156

Might as well try to send a St. Bernard down a rathole."

"And now you're going down there, sir?"

"Yes, with a fleet of shallow-draft vessels. Anywhere a pirate can go, I can follow."

"Good! And thank you for giving me a chance!"

The commodore smiled. "Want to stay at Meridian Hill till we're ready to sail?"

"Er—I thought I'd go to Norfolk for a bit, sir."

"I see. Don't you think Susan Marchant is a little young to think about love and marriage?"

It was no use trying to fool the commodore. "I'd never propose to her, sir, till I was a lieutenant."

"Good idea. Her cousin tells me Susan thinks of you as a big brother. Better to keep it that way for a while, eh?"

"Yes, sir!"

The first person Glasgow saw in Norfolk was Susan coming down the street, smiling up at a six-foot-two lieutenant.

She sparkled. She introduced them to each other. Ted was stationed at the Navy Yard; Glasgow was her favorite big brother!

The tall lieutenant had a bone-crushing handshake and a smile full of white teeth. He said any big brother of Susan's was a friend of his!

I'd like to meet you with pistols at twenty paces! Glasgow thought.

157

He saw Susan several times in the next weeks—always with the tall lieutenant.

He was glad when Commodore Porter's fleet was ready to sail. Once more Midshipman Farragut was acting lieutenant, second in command, this time on the schooner *Greyhound*. How many more times, he wondered, would he command the crew of a ship and still be only a midshipman?

The *Greyhound* sailed in a howling nor'easter. On deck, Glasgow shivered and thought longingly of the warm Caribbean. Soon he was in the Caribbean, thinking longingly of a cool breeze—even of a nor'easter. Anything to escape the sweltering heat! All day the sun beat down. The seams of the deck oozed tar. At night Glasgow never slept below deck. He spread a tarpaulin or a piece of canvas to protect his uniform, used a roll of anything handy for a pillow, and slept topside. Yes, it was hot, dirty, dangerous work.

Sailing offshore was bad enough where they had sea room and the lookout could sight a sail in the distance. Working inshore was worse, searching inlets, bays, and coves for pirate hideouts. Inshore the schooner must inch along with a leadsman sounding constantly to guard against reefs and shoals, and the lookouts must be on the alert to guard against ambuscades.

Glasgow began to worry about the men. They

were near the breaking point. He could hear it in their voices. Whenever a man wanted to talk to him, he was always ready to listen.

It was the ones who didn't talk that worried him most—the ones who didn't sleep, or who slept and had nightmares.

Ben Livington was one who didn't talk. At last one night he said, "Mr. Farragut, sir, have you got a few minutes?"

"All the time in the world."

"How long is this going to keep on?" Ben asked. "I mean—this business of always feeling danger breathing on the back of your neck? A battle is one thing. You get in, fight, and get out. Either you come through or you don't. But this! Day in, day out, prowling around into all these hidey-holes. Feeling like maybe eyes are watching you!"

Glasgow let him talk it out and saw him finally relax.

New orders came. Mr. Farragut was transferred to the commodore's flagship, the *Seagull*. She was a steamer, the first one ever to see service in action in the navy. It would be a new experience, all right, but Glasgow didn't know whether he was glad or sorry. Who would look after his men on the *Greyhound*? He only hoped the next executive officer would be patient and ready to listen.

The sailors of the *Seagull* growled. They had to

admit she could get into and out of places where a sailing ship might be in danger. They would admit the *Seagull* was never becalmed and never in danger of being driven onto a lee shore by a contrary wind. But that was all they could say for her. They hated the smoke and cinders that fouled their clean white decks.

The commodore was planning another raid on the hideouts of the pirates when the curse of the Caribbean struck—yellow fever. The surgeon of the fleet worked desperately, and Glasgow worked with him. Years ago, as a boy of twelve, he had worked with the wounded after a battle. This was worse. For the first time he saw the ghastly climax of yellow fever and knew why men called it "the black vomit." Was this how his mother had died?

The death toll of the yellow fever was worse than the death toll of that battle too; more than ninety per cent of the men who sickened of it died.

Commodore Porter was stricken. For days he lay between life and death. Finally he began to mend, but he was far too weak to return to duty. He turned his command over to another and went home on the *Seagull*. Glasgow went with him.

"You've been a godsend," the commodore said. "Thank heaven you didn't come down with it too."

The *Seagull* was in sight of Washington when Glasgow wakened in the night with a pounding

160

headache. Men carried him off the ship. For days he lay in a hospital.

Once he heard a doctor say, "Don't think he'll pull through."

I wish I'd told Susan I love her, Glasgow thought.

Finally the doctor said, "Looks like you'll make it."

I'm going to tell her! Glasgow said to himself.

When he could walk without holding on to something, he went to Norfolk and straight to the Marchant home.

Susan opened the door and gasped. "Glasgow!" She put an arm around him. "Come in and sit down before you fall down!" She led him to a chair, then sat on a footstool at his feet. "What happened?"

"Yellow fever."

"It must have been awful!"

"It was. It hit twenty-five officers. Twenty-three died."

"Oh, no! What if you had died? I'd want to die too!"

He reached for her hands and pressed them to his cheek. "Dear Susan. I wanted to be all ship-shape when I saw you. Looking masterful. I didn't want to look like . . ."

"Like an end of frayed rope? Well, you do. But

—why did you want to look masterful?''

"I wanted to say 'I love you and will you marry me when I'm a lieutenant?' "

"Not necessarily."

"Oh . . ."

"I might even marry you *before* you're a lieutenant."

"Susan!"

"Dear Glasgow, it doesn't matter what you *are*! Because I know what you're going to be! You're going clear to the top!"

"Thirteen years a midshipman. At this rate I'll be old and gray before I'm even a commander."

"You'll get there!"

"Maybe—if I get enough sea duty. I'm no scholar. But with enough sea duty, I may get somewhere."

"Sea duty, please!" Susan said. Then she added, "Just so it's not the West Indies!"

Presently orders came. The West Indies.

"Please, please don't get sick again!"

"Not much danger of that," he told her. "People don't seem to get yellow fever twice."

Yellow fever was not the only disease of the West Indies. Again Glasgow survived the tour of duty and fell ill in sight of Washington. This time it was malaria.

The same doctor happened to take care of him. "Tell your Navy Department that this is enough service in the West Indies for you. Another tour of duty down there and they can scratch one officer!"

Once more, when he could walk without hanging onto something, he went to Norfolk, looking like "an end of frayed rope."

"Glasgow!" And Susan was in his arms.

In September he wrote to Commodore Porter: "I didn't keep my promise about not proposing to Susan till I was a lieutenant. I even married her."

The commodore's answer came in a hurry. He wanted to meet Susan. The whole family did. Wouldn't Glasgow and Susan spend a part of their honeymoon at Meridian Hill?

Mrs. Porter opened her arms to Susan and said, "Glasgow, you lucky man! But you deserve a lovely wife!"

"Susan," the commodore said, "you're good for Glasgow. I've known him since he was eight years old, and I've never seen him look so happy."

"Do you really think so?" Susan asked. "The minute we got married he asked for sea duty."

The commodore stared.

Susan began to laugh. "I hope he does get sea duty because he loves it. Anywhere but in the West Indies though! He's had enough of that!"

"Yes," the commodore said. "It's hot, dirty, dangerous work." Then before Glasgow could stop him, he talked about reefs and shoals and ambuscades of pirates. Susan's eyes got bigger and bigger. "And the worst of it," the commodore said, "is that we can't stop the pirates till we can take care of the 'honest' people who trade with them! The respectable citizens who help the pirates profit by their murders! Merchants can buy cargo at half price from pirates, so they shut their eyes to where the cargoes come from. The mayors of the towns—"alcaldes" they call them—well, the pirates know how to grease palms. So the alcaldes shut their eyes too."

"I hope somebody mops up the earth with a few greasy-palmed alcaldes!"

The commodore chuckled. "Glasgow, we ought to get Susan on the Board of Navy Commissioners."

In December Glasgow and Susan remembered that talk with the commodore when they heard of the incident at Fajardo, Puerto Rico.

Pirates had landed there and robbed an Anglo merchant of over $5,000. Lieutenant Platt of the U.S. *Beagle* went ashore to talk to the alcalde about the robbery. Policemen in Fajardo seized the lieutenant, put him in jail, finally released him, and booted him out of town. The alcalde looked the other way.

Commodore Porter was in the Caribbean. He

swooped down on Fajardo with a squadron of marines and forced the alcalde to apologize to Lieutenant Platt.

"Good for Commodore Porter!" Susan's eyes glowed. "I'll bet he gets a promotion out of this!"

"He can't," Glasgow told her. "He has the top rank now. Even commodore is just a courtesy title. But they might strike a medal for him, or something like that."

"When they do, let's go to Washington and help celebrate! That will be a happy, happy day!"

In January they had an unexpected "happy, happy day." Glasgow got his promotion to lieutenant.

"I knew it, I knew it!" Susan said. "Next stop commander!"

"Fifteen years a midshipman; I wonder how long a lieutenant?"

For a moment Susan looked angry. "Yes, when I think that you were an acting lieutenant six years ago . . ." She stopped. "But I'm not going to be mad at the navy now. I'm too happy."

In March Susan was blazing again. Commodore Porter had been recalled to Washington to face a court-martial over his "conduct in the Fajardo incident."

"I don't believe it!" she stormed. "*I don't believe it!*"

But it was true. In May the verdict was handed

down: Commodore Porter was suspended for six months.

Susan was so furious she wept.

Glasgow was heartsick, but he tried to explain. "It's all mixed up with international politics, Susan. The Monroe Doctrine. President Monroe declared we'd not allow any European countries to invade territories of the Americas—colonies that had rebelled and won their freedom. But some territories—Cuba and Puerto Rico, for instance—still belong to Spain. When Commodore Porter marched into Fajardo, the Spanish ambassador raised cain. The United States had invaded European territory."

"You mean the Spanish ambassador is standing up for a greasy-palmed alcalde? But we can't stand up for our Lieutenant Platt? Right now I hate the navy!"

"Susan! You must never say a thing like that!"

"You say what you want to, and I'll think what I want to!"

She simmered in silence until Glasgow's orders came. He would serve as a deck officer on the new frigate, *Brandywine*, which would have the honor of taking General Lafayette home to France after his triumphant tour of the United States.

Glasgow told Susan of how he'd heard of Lafayette when he was a little boy and how his father had been "just like Lafayette, only greater." He smiled. "Lafayette's name has been like a shining star to me all these years. Now I'll get to sail with him."

"Oh, Glasgow . . ." She hesitated, then smiled. "I guess I do love the navy."

"Of course you do."

He took Susan with him to see the *Brandywine*. "She's beautiful!" Susan said.

"Wait till she spreads all her sails. Then she'll be the most beautiful thing man ever made."

"Dear Glasgow, I'll never say it again, about hating the navy!"

"Of course not, dear."

"This won't be dangerous, like service in the West Indies, will it?"

"It'll be like a pleasure cruise!"

As the *Brandywine* sailed Glasgow stood on deck, took a deep breath of cool, fresh air, and smiled to himself. Finally a lieutenant! And sailing on the *Brandywine*, the most beautiful ship in the navy!

Four days out when the quartermaster held the glass to check their speed, he said, "It's my guess, sir, that we've got the fastest ship in the navy!"

In the middle of the night the bosun's pipe shrilled and voices bellowed, "All hands on deck!"

Glasgow leaped from his bunk, lurched across

the cabin, and realized they had run into a storm.
He dressed and hurried topside. The wind and
rain hit him so hard that he gasped and turned
away for a moment to catch his breath. He hadn't
felt anything like this since Cape Horn weather. It
wasn't as cold, but if possible the wind was blowing harder. The *Brandywine* wallowed and rolled
until her yards almost touched the water.

Men lay aloft to reef sails and ease the laboring
ship.

A man stumbled up from below, shouting,
"She's leaking!"

Four crews took turns at the pumps, working at
top speed.

Another report from below. "The leak's gaining
on us!" They'd have to lighten ship. Men lurched
down the hatchways. Soon they formed a line, and
an endless stream of cannon balls passed from
hand to hand and went over the side.

At last good word from below: They were holding their own against the leak—if they could keep
up the pace at the pumps. Dawn came; the day
passed; night fell again. Still the storm raged. It
was after midnight when the storm died down, the
rain stopped, the skies cleared, and the wind came
fresh from the west again—fresh and steady.

Glasgow left the deck so tired he was stagger-
ing. And I'm the one, he thought, who said this

168

would be just a pleasure cruise! Any man who sailed anywhere could never know what the sea had in store for him!

After two days of fair weather everything was shipshape again; the leaks stopped, stores dried out, and the storm almost forgotten.

When the *Brandywine* had completed her mission, she wintered in the Mediterranean. Every now and then another ship challenged her to a race. Soon the word passed. The *Brandywine* was not only the fastest ship in the U.S. Navy: She was doubtless the fastest ship in the world!

In April of 1826 the *Brandywine* came to anchor off New York. What next, Glasgow wondered. If only he could get a brief leave home, then sail on the *Brandywine* again! But that was too much good luck to hope for.

A boat brought dispatches and orders. Lieutenant Farragut would stand by until the *Telltale* was ready for sea. He would take her to Norfolk, have six days' leave, then return to the *Brandywine*.

His lucky star had really risen. He wrote the good news to Susan and sent his letter by a ship just clearing for Norfolk. Then he looked at the rest of his mail.

There was a letter from Commodore Porter. Smiling, he opened it—and his face went blank. The commodore had been offered the post of Gen-

169

eral of the Marines—Admiral—of the Mexican Navy. He was going to Mexico to survey the situation. If he liked what he found, he'd resign from the U.S. Navy and stay. He was taking two of his boys with him—Thomas and David Dixon.

No, no, no! Glasgow thought, he can't do that! The news took the edge off his happiness.

But as the *Telltale* neared Norfolk he forgot everything but Susan. Had she had time to get his letter? Would she be waiting there to meet him? He scanned the wharf for a glimpse of her face, her smile, her sparkling eyes.

Dr. Bedford greeted him as he went ashore. "I want to talk to you, Mr. Farragut. If you'll come to my office—"

"Later!" Glasgow beamed. "I have six days' leave! I'll see you tomorrow!"

The doctor did not answer his smile. "I must see you before you see Susan."

A knot twisted in the pit of Glasgow's stomach. "What's wrong? She's sick?"

"Yes. Come along to my office, please."

15. "WE WHO WANDER
ABOUT THE WORLD"

The doctor said nothing else until they were in his office. "Mr. Farragut, your wife is very ill. Arthritis."

"What caused it?"

"Nobody knows."

"How do you cure it?"

"We can't."

"You mean—she'll die of it?"

"Sometimes she'll wish she could die she'll be in so much pain. It's a hellish business. And we can't do a thing! There are no safe drugs to ease the pain."

"Someone, somewhere, can do something!"

"I know how you feel." The doctor sighed. "You'll try everything. But nothing will help."

"I'll take her to the best doctors in the country!"

"I know. And they'll tell you what I've told you."

"But what can I do?"

"Let her lie to you. Pretend to believe her."

"Susan never told a lie in her life!"

"She's telling them now." The doctor's eyes were sad. "Her favorite expression is 'much better.' She's either 'much better' right then or she's going to be 'much better' tomorrow. It's rough enough on a doctor who loves her. God help you, Mr. Farragut."

Glasgow sat with his face in his hands.

"It's all you can do. Agree with her. She's 'much better'—even if she breaks out in a cold sweat from the pain. Joke with her. Find something funny to tell her every time you enter the room."

Numb with shock, Glasgow went to the Marchants' home.

Susan was sitting in the window, watching for him. She smiled. He forced himself to smile, to wave, to race up the steps and into the house.

"Susan!"

She got up from the chair, but she did not run to meet him. He hurried to her and put his arms around her. She rested her head on his chest for a moment, then she looked up and smiled at him.

"Serves me right, doesn't it? Remember when I said you looked like 'an end of frayed rope'? Now I do!"

He steadied her as she sat down. He pulled up a stool and sat at her feet. "No, you don't! You're beautiful!"

"You're such a lovely liar," she said. "But I'm so glad you're here! I feel much better already!"

"Of course you do!"

And Glasgow, who had been so eager for duty on the *Brandywine*, asked to be relieved of it and given a leave of absence. He took Susan to the doctors at the Medical College of Yale. Dr. Bedford was right. They could do nothing.

That fall when they returned to Norfolk he was glad his assignment was for shore duty—second in command on the receiving ship *Alert* at Norfolk.

"Are you sorry about shore duty?" she asked.

"I'm delighted. I can probably get home for a while almost every day!"

He reported to Captain Kennedy in charge of the *Alert*.

"Mr. Farragut," the captain said, "I'm having quarters prepared for you and your wife on the *Alert*. You can be with her much more than if she were on shore."

When Glasgow could trust his voice not to shake he said, "Thank you, sir. Thank you!"

"We only wish we could do something that would really help!"

When Susan heard about it she said, "That dear man! You know, I *do* love the navy!"

173

Quarters on board the *Alert* did give him a chance to spend much more time with Susan. He remembered the doctor's orders. He always tried to have something special to tell her when he went to their cabin.

One evening he said, "We have more than three dozen boys who want to be sailors. I'm going to open a school for them."

"To teach them navigation?"

"To teach them to read and write."

"You mean they can't?"

"Most of them can't. I've an idea that's why they want to join the navy. They don't like school." He smiled. "I remember the feeling, sitting in the schoolroom with my mind a thousand miles away. My teachers tried, but they didn't get very far with me."

"Do you think you'll get farther with these boys?"

"I have one advantage. My word is law."

He started teaching the boys with words that would mean something to them. On a big piece of tarpaulin he had a frigate outlined in white paint, with words printed on it.

Most of the boys began to get interested. Only Hank Weber, the oldest of the boys, refused to learn.

"No!" he shouted. "I won't go to school! I left home so I wouldn't have to go to school!"

174

"You're going to school now," Glasgow told him. "That's an order."

Hank spoke through his teeth. "You can make me sit in the schoolroom, sir, but you can't make me learn, sir!"

Day after day Hank sat. When Glasgow asked him a question he said, "I don't know, sir."

A month passed. One day a boy stumbled over a word.

Suddenly Hank yelled, "It's *mizzen*, you fool! It's *mizzen*!"

All the boys clapped. Hank flushed and grinned. After that he worked as though to make up for lost time. Soon he was reading with the best of them, and he had a special knack with figures. When Hank left the *Alert* he went as yeoman to a ship's purser.

After two years on the receiving ship, Glasgow's orders came for sea duty.

"That's wonderful!" Susan said.

"You really don't mind?"

"Of course not. Remember what you said? The more sea duty the faster you'll rise? Maybe you'll come back a commander!"

He took her to stay with her family.

Susan smiled when she said good-bye. "I'm really improving. When you get back I'll be much better!"

"Of course, dear."

175

So the heartbreaking years passed: shore duty and Susan with him on a receiving ship, sea duty and coming home each time to find Susan more helpless.

News of Commodore Porter had been heartbreaking too. The Mexican government had not lived up to its promise. Young Thomas had died of yellow fever. The commodore had come home bankrupt and broken in health. Meridian Hill had to be sold for debts. Mrs. Porter and the younger children were living at Green Bank. Commodore Porter was an exile—United States Minister to faraway Turkey.

There was one bright spot in those dark years. One day in Norfolk a tall broad-shouldered young man called out, "Mr. Farragut, sir!" He came toward Glasgow, beaming and holding out his hand.

Glasgow shook hands, then said, "I'm afraid you're mistaking me for someone else. My brother William, perhaps?"

"Oh, no, sir! I know you all right!" He grinned. "Remember Hank Weber, the boy that wasn't going to learn?"

"Hank!" It was not just that Hank had grown taller and broader. He was ramrod straight, with an air of command. "Tell me what's been happening to you!"

Hank had done a hitch in the navy, he said, and then had signed on an East Indiaman. "The captain and his mate were fine fellows. The mate taught me navigation. With Bowditch's book. You know those tables. Even with just arithmetic I could work out problems in navigation.

"Well, in Batavia the captain died, and the mate took sick. When he knew he wasn't going to make it, he called the crew together. 'Mr. Weber is the man who can get you home,' he told them. 'Promise you'll obey his orders.' They promised."

Hank smiled. "The funniest thing—till then I was always just 'Hank,' but from that minute on I was 'Mr. Weber.' Well, we got back to New York all right. The owners certainly were pleased."

"I'd think so!" Glasgow said.

"Now I'm master of a ship on the New York-Charleston run. In command of my own ship! How's that?"

"You've made this a red-letter day for me!" Glasgow told him. I can do with a few red-letter days, he thought.

In 1838 Glasgow was on duty in the Gulf of Mexico with Commodore Dallas. The navy was keeping an eye on affairs in Mexico and Texas. Santa Anna, who had talked of freedom and justice, had become a savage dictator. Texas had re-

177

belled against him, and Sam Houston had defeated him at the Battle of San Jacinto. Texas was an independent republic now, but affairs were in a pretty chaotic state.

Commodore Dallas sent for Glasgow. "Mr. Farragut, I believe you speak both French and Spanish?"

"Yes, sir."

"Then I need you for special duty." The French, he said, were blockading the Mexican coast, demanding payment of debts. "You'll be able to deal with men on both sides of the question and see that our citizens are protected."

Soon Glasgow, in command of the sloop *Erie*, was dealing with Mexicans ashore and with the French in their ships. In November the French sent an ultimatum to the Mexican government; affairs would be settled by November 27, or the French would attack the castle of San Juan.

The deadline came. The battle began. At first the French tried mortar fire. Big shells, lobbed high in the air, fell inside the walls and exploded. They did not seem to silence the guns of San Juan. Then the French used horizontal fire, smashing shells into the walls. That was a different story. The shells buried themselves in the thick walls, then exploded, tearing great holes. A few hours of that and San Juan would be rubble! The fort surrendered.

178

After the battle Glasgow had a chance to visit San Juan. He studied the difference in damage of mortar fire and horizontal shelling. Then he visited one of the French ships. A young lieutenant showed him their latest improvements in guns. Glasgow went back to the *Erie*, thinking hard.

That night he started a long letter to Commodore Barron to report on all he had learned. It took him several sessions to write it and make a copy of it. He wore glasses now for close work, but he still could not read or write very long at a time. He ended his letter with a plea for the United States to wake up.

If we who wander about the world do not keep those at home informed of the daily improvements in other navies, how can we hope to improve? Particularly when we see men with the idea that because they once gained a victory they can do it again? So they may. But I can tell them it must be with the means of 1838 and not with those of 1812!

He told Commodore Barron he was leaving for home soon and could be reached in Norfolk.

He went home with a mixture of hope and dread. Susan was always so sure she would be better soon. This time when he got home, she was a little pain-racked skeleton, so helpless that he had to carry her in his arms.

179

"It's so good you're home!" she whispered. "I feel better already. And you'll tell me all about it, won't you?"

He told her of being sent in command of the *Erie* because he could speak both French and Spanish.

"French and Spanish both! I'll bet their eyes popped out!"

"They certainly did!" And he told her about the letter to Commodore Barron. "That's going to wake up the navy!"

"What did the commodore say?"

"I haven't had an answer yet. But I'll hear soon. He'll probably call me to Washington to talk things over. I'll sit at a big table with a lot of important men. I'll talk and they'll listen!"

"I hope it's real soon!"

But weeks lengthened into months and no word came from Commodore Barron. Glasgow thought up excuses to explain it to Susan: Maybe the commodore had turned the letter over to the Secretary of the Navy. Maybe the Secretary was studying it. Maybe the Secretary had turned it over to the Board of Navy Commissioners. Maybe . . .

In 1840 Susan died.

Glasgow wrote immediately to the Secretary of the Navy. He asked for sea duty. Anything to get away from Norfolk!

16. VIRGINIA

In February his orders came. Lieutenant Farragut would report to the *Delaware* for a tour of duty in the South Atlantic. He would be executive officer —second in command. Glasgow smiled at that. It would be his most important duty to date. The *Delaware* was one of the big ones—two thousand tons—seventy-four guns. She would have over eight hundred officers and men when she was ready for sea.

A skeleton crew brought her to the Navy Yard. He'd have to complete his crew, then train his men in every maneuver of handling sails and guns.

Lord, give me the wisdom of Solomon! he said to himself.

He lived on the *Delaware*. Generally he was up

with the first sailors in the morning; often he paced the deck with the watch at night.

He still remembered his visit to the French ship off San Juan. Now he looked at every task on the *Delaware*, asking himself, Is there a better way to do this?

The powder boys—running from the magazines deep in the hold up to the gun decks and the spar deck—was there a better way to get the powder up? He designed a hoist to bring the powder from the hold.

His men looked blank when he talked of the hoist. "But, sir, we always have—"

He smiled. "Just because we always *have* doesn't mean we always *have to*, does it?"

The carpenters looked blank too when he sketched what he wanted built, but they built it. They had to.

When the first hoist was ready, they tried it. The men stared, shot sidelong glances at one another, then grinned. It worked!

He watched the men wrestling with the half tops—the heavy platforms that held the shrouds of the top masts. The platforms were made in two half-circles, hauled up, then bolted together around the head of the mast. He watched as the men struggled with the heavy platforms and the tangle of lines. It took them half a day to do the job.

I wonder . . . he said to himself. It took him more than a week to work out his new method. He explained it to the men.

"But, sir, we always have—" Then a man grinned. "Just because we always *have* doesn't mean we always *have to*, does it?"

They practiced the new maneuver. The day came when they did the job in twenty minutes. Word of that feat spread through the Norfolk Navy Yard. Men came by the dozens to watch it done.

When the *Delaware* was shipshape and her crew complete, they piped Captain Macauley aboard and went out on a training cruise.

Scarcely a man had ever handled big guns before. Glasgow remembered his first gun drill. He told the captains of his gun crews to run through the orders for handling a gun until every man could repeat them. Maybe that would make the training go faster.

It didn't help much. The men were all thumbs. Every man got in somebody's way. It took half an hour to loose a broadside. Drill, drill, drill! The men hauled on the tackles till they dropped on the deck and lay panting. They were still too slow.

For the first time Glasgow had some understanding of Creighton's savage impatience on the *Washington*. When a man commanded a ship, she was part of him. Working with a lubberly crew was as frustrating as trying to walk on a foot that had "gone to sleep."

Once he had said "Give me the wisdom of Solomon!" Now he said "Give me the patience of Job!"

Patience finally paid off. After two months the gun crews could loose three broadsides in four minutes, and he hadn't broken their spirit in the process of training them. They were as proud of the *Delaware* as he was.

One day a dispatch boat brought letters to Captain Macauley. The captain asked for all hands on deck. He unfolded a paper and read. Lieutenant Farragut was now Commander Farragut.

The *Delaware* rang with cheers. Fellow officers crowded around to shake hands. Glasgow could only smile, wordless. He was remembering Susan and her shining belief, and fighting a lump in his throat.

Forty years old—thirty-one years in the navy. I wonder, he thought, if I'll live long enough to become a captain?

The summer of 1842 when the *Delaware* was still on her South Atlantic station, Glasgow was detached from that duty and sent to the *Decatur*. Just a little ship—only five hundred tons—but he smiled. She was his to command!

She had just come in from a long cruise; most of her crew were going home; he must overhaul her and train a new crew. Once more the patient drill. At last he took her out on a shakedown cruise. He came back beaming. The *Decatur* might be small, but she was the smartest ship in the squadron.

Late that year the *Decatur* was in the harbor of Rio, getting ready to clear for home with dispatches. His crew, swaggering with pride, got her ready in jig time. The morning they were scheduled to sail, both wind and tide were against them, and they were boxed in on all sides.

The First looked worried. "What about it, sir?"

Glasgow reached for the trumpet. "I think we'll give them something to talk about!"

Glasgow told his men what they were going to do—box-haul the *Decatur* out of the harbor. It took split-second timing, he said, but they were just the men who could do it! They would out-*Decatur* the *Decatur*!

The men cheered. They moved like streaks, carrying out his orders. All around the *Decatur*, men on other ships watched and shook their heads. When the *Decatur* cleared the harbor, everybody cheered.

The crew of the *Decatur* were so proud they strutted standing still. "Wait till Norfolk hears about this!"

Norfolk . . . if only he didn't have to go back to Norfolk. But orders were orders.

When he came to anchor off Norfolk, he paid off his crew, then sent the *Decatur* to the Navy Yard for overhaul.

Friends hailed him. "Welcome home, Commander!"

Home . . . He had no home. He'd take the first boat for Washington and ask for sea duty again.

As he turned toward the wharf an imperious voice called "Commander Farragut!" It was Mrs. Stone—tall, white-haired, regal as a queen. Some said she was quite a leader; others said she was the world's worst martinet.

She'll not get very far giving me orders, Glasgow thought. Whatever she says, I'll say, "No, thank you, Mrs. Stone! Thank you very much, Mrs. Stone, but *no!*"

"Commander," she said, "I'm not going to dwell on sad things. I just wanted to tell you what one woman said when Susan died. She said, 'When Mr. Farragut dies, there should be a monument for him, reaching to the heavens, built by every wife in Norfolk putting in one stone!' "

Glasgow could not answer.

"No more of that!" she said. "Come along. There is someone I want you to meet."

And Glasgow, who had vowed to say no to any order from her, said "Yes, Mrs. Stone," and followed obediently.

The "someone he was to meet" was Virginia

Loyall, a tall, slender young woman with smooth dark hair, a serene face, and level gray eyes.

"I do want you to get acquainted," Mrs. Stone said. Then she gave neither of them a chance to get a word in edgewise. She talked and talked.

Virginia listened gravely, and said "Yes, Mrs. Stone" and "No, Mrs. Stone" in the right places.

Presently Mrs. Stone said, "Commander, the town is agog about your feat in bringing your ship out of the harbor in Rio! I want you to tell us *all* about it!"

Glasgow smiled. "Yes, Mrs. Stone! You see, it was this way: We were rather hemmed in. Rat Island on the starboard beam, a Brazilian frigate on our larboard, a sloop of war on our starboard quarter but nearly astern, and a large merchant-man on our larboard quarter. You get the picture, don't you?"

"Er—yes." For once Mrs. Stone sounded a little uncertain.

"Then there were other complications. The tide was running flood and the wind south. We were lying in eleven-and-a-half fathoms of water. You can see how that would complicate things, can't you?"

"Er—quite." Mrs. Stone sounded dazed.

"Now, the maneuver was this," Glasgow went on. "We hove a short stay, set the topsails, braced the head yards slightly aback on a larboard tack, braced the after yards sharp up on the starboard tack, and—"

Mrs. Stone interrupted. She was so sorry, but she had just remembered something she had promised to do. She hurried away.

Virginia Loyall began laughing. "Congratulations, Commander. That's the first time anybody ever got ahead of Mrs. Stone!"

Glasgow laughed too. He strolled along with Virginia, and she brought him up-to-date on Norfolk. She had a dry sense of humor that went with her grave face and level eyes. He found himself laughing again.

At the Loyall home he said good-bye. He was going to Washington, he told her, to ask for sea duty again.

"Maybe when you come back," she said, "you'll have more information for Mrs. Stone. I hope I get to hear the conversation."

He went down the street, chuckling to himself.

In Washington the Secretary of the Navy was polite but regretful. There was no ship available for the commander at that time. Commander Farragut would be on leave, awaiting orders.

After a few restless days in Washington he returned to Norfolk. He strolled past the Loyall home, but it looked like it was closed. He asked—in a very offhand way—if anybody had seen Virginia Loyall. The first people he asked did not know where she was; some others thought she was out of town. Finally someone said, "Virginia Loyall? Oh, she's gone up in the mountains to Farquier Springs."

Days dragged in Norfolk. Glasgow wrote to the Navy Department. Commander Farragut was going to Farquier Springs. He would await orders there.

When he arrived, the first person he saw was Virginia.

Her eyes widened. "Why, Commander Farragut! I thought you'd be halfway around the world by now! What a surprise!"

"And what a surprise to see you! A delightful surprise!" He'd brought that off rather well he thought.

A man from Norfolk ambled by. He hailed Glasgow cheerfully. "You found her all right, did you, Commander?" He beamed at Virginia. "He was asking all over Norfolk about you." He meandered off.

Glasgow could feel his face getting hot. "We have an expression in the navy—'to stand off and on.'"

"Good heavens, you're not going to explain it to me, are you?" she pleaded.

"No, but I'm not going to try to stand off and on when I talk to you either."

A young lieutenant came up. He called Glasgow

"sir" and reminded Virginia that the dance was at eight that night. He was very helpful. Had the commander just arrived? Would he like a partner for the dance that night? The young lieutenant's aunt was there. Probably younger than the commander but good fun and a fine dancer.

Glasgow thanked the young lieutenant. He had some reports to catch up on that evening he said. He doubted if he could get to the dance.

That night he twiddled his thumbs in his room until nine thirty, then went to the dance.

Old friends from Norfolk greeted him warmly and introduced him to charming young ladies.

One captain said to his wife, "It's a calculated risk, but I'll let you have one dance with Commander Farragut. Just one!"

Virginia's young lieutenant was not so kind.

But a captain pulled rank on the young lieutenant, claimed Virginia, and then introduced Commander Farragut.

"We've met," Glasgow said.

"So I heard!" The captain chuckled, slapped him on the back, and went his way.

"Did you get your reports done, Commander?" Virginia asked.

"I'll not stand off and on about it. I didn't have any reports. I just wasn't going to let your lieutenant arrange my life for me. Is there a dance tomorrow night? And are you engaged for it?"

190

"Yes. . . . But perhaps I could say *I* have reports to do."

When they went back to Norfolk, Glasgow reported his whereabouts to the Navy Department and asked for further leave of absence. In December he and Virginia were married. Almost on the heels of the ceremony, orders came.

Virginia stared at the letter and caught her breath. He opened it. Commander Farragut would report to the Norfolk Navy Yard for duty.

A year later their little son was born.

"Not just because he's ours," Glasgow said, "but Loyall is the handsomest baby I've ever seen. And the best baby, too!"

"I explained that to him," Virginia said. "I told him he'd have to be very good at first because later his father would spoil him to death!"

New orders. They looked at each other. Slowly Glasgow opened the letter. He would take command of the receiving ship *Pennsylvania* in Norfolk.

"We're so lucky!" she said.

He arranged quarters for them on the *Pennsylvania*. The sailors called Loyall the "Little Luff." They carved toys for him of ivory, bone, and wood. They accused one another of spoiling him.

"What a wonderful place to bring up a little boy!" Virginia said. "I'd like for him to spend his first five years on a receiving ship!"

But in 1845, before Loyall was a year old, Glasgow was writing to the Navy Department asking for sea duty. War was coming. He was sure of that. The United States was going to annex Texas. That would mean war with Mexico. And he'd surely get a command when war came. Nobody had had more experience down there than he had had!

He did not tell Virginia about it. No use worrying her until he got orders.

17. SHORE DUTY

In a letter to the Secretary of the Navy, Glasgow
listed all his service in the West Indies and off the
coast of Mexico. He knew Fort San Juan that
guarded Vera Cruz; he had inspected the fort; he
had sounded the waters around it. He could speak
Spanish. He hoped, if any trouble developed, he
might have a command. He sent the letter.

No answer.

In 1846 war began. He wrote again—and again.
In March of 1847—almost a year after war had
begun—orders came. Commander Farragut would
take charge of the sloop *Saratoga*, now being readied for sea, and report for duty off San Juan.

He scoured the receiving ship, the Navy Yard,
even the wharves and streets of Norfolk for a

crew. When he was ready to sail—still ten per cent short of a full crew—only one of his sailors was rated an able seaman.

So . . . he'd train them! He'd trained men before; he could do it again. Patience—enthusiasm—and by the time they reached San Juan they'd be on their toes!

Virginia wasn't sleeping well. There were dark circles under her eyes. "You're not worrying, are you?" he asked.

"I'm scared to death!" she admitted. "But that's what I get for marrying a naval officer, isn't it?"

He kissed her and little Loyall good-bye and sailed with his crew of landlubbers. All the way down the coast and across the Gulf of Mexico— drill, drill, drill. As they neared San Juan he was smiling. Bless those men, they could pass for sailors. They were really good with the guns. At the signal they could loose their guns, fire a round, secure their guns, and be back at their stations as fast as any crew he'd ever trained.

When the lookout called, "Land ho-o-o-o!" the crew crowded forward for a first glimpse of Fort San Juan. A gasp, then a groan ran over the ship. The American flag was flying over San Juan.

Glasgow heard the mutters of disgust and re-membered when Bainbridge's squadron entered the Mediterranean ready for action against the

194

Barbary pirates—only to find the war was over. He remembered the letdown in the spirits of the men. This letdown would be worse. His men weren't regular navy men trained in a long tradition. They were just landlubbers he had brought to a fighting pitch—and all for nothing.

The *Saratoga* got orders: blockade off Tuxpan. In spite of the heat, Glasgow shivered. Nothing was so deadly dull as blockade duty. He could only pray that he could keep up the spirits of his men.

He could not. Day after day they lay offshore in the sweltering heat. Nothing to do. Just be on the lookout for enemy ships that never came. Never in his life had he had to punish so many men as he punished in the next few months.

Then yellow fever struck. Soon a fourth of his men were down. On the heels of the yellow fever —a hurricane. The *Saratoga* had to head for the open sea to escape being driven onto a lee shore.

At last his duty ended. He went home to Norfolk.

Virginia ran to his arms and then wept. "It's been so *long*!"

Long? Yes, he thought grimly. Not quite a year, but it seemed like ten. May Heaven deliver me from ever commanding a ship on blockade duty again! Nothing but a long sea voyage—preferably clear around the world—would wipe out the taste of those months.

"I hope you don't have to go to sea very soon again!"

He kissed her and didn't say what he was thinking.

Orders: Shore duty. The Norfolk Navy Yard again.

He forced himself to smile.

Three times in the next six years orders came for shore duty. Glasgow decided that his long-ago letter to Commodore Barron must have come to someone's attention. He had written about improvements in gunnery. Now . . .

Orders: To Washington to help write a book on ordnance.

Orders: To Point Comfort to run tests on guns.

Orders: To the Norfolk Navy Yard to lecture on gunnery.

One night in the summer of 1854 he sat down at his desk to write a letter to the Navy Department. Enough was enough. He was going to ask—no, he was going to *demand* sea duty! Four times he tried to start the letter. He couldn't think. It was too hot, and his head was hammering. Maybe tomorrow morning . . .

When he wakened, the afternoon sun was shining into their bedroom. Virginia was sitting by the

196

bed. He said, "I must have slept all night and half the day."

"You've slept quite a few nights." Something in Virginia's voice was different. She was worried.

"What's wrong?"

"Nothing now. You've had cholera. You've been very sick. But you're on the mend."

"Then what's worrying you? Don't stand off and on about it!"

"Oh, darling, I've been so thoughtless! I never realized how you hated shore duty."

"Now what ever gave you that idea?"

"And don't *you* stand off and on about it! It was all you talked about when you were delirious."

"It's true," he admitted. "Maybe I don't like shore duty because desk work is hard for me. But even before I had trouble with my eyes, I was more of a—a—"

"A man of action? Dear, I'm sorry I've been so thoughtless."

"Bless you, you couldn't have done anything about it. I get orders. I obey."

"But I could have helped you explode about it!" she said.

He laughed and felt better.

When the doctor came, Virginia asked, "How soon can Commander Farragut have sea duty?"

The doctor blinked. "Now that's the first time I

ever heard a navy wife ask that."

"So now you've heard it!" Virginia said. "How soon can he have sea duty?"

"He won't be ready for *any* duty for quite a while."

The doctor was still there when a letter came for Glasgow. Virginia opened it to read it to him. Commander Farragut was to go to the far Northwest to build a Navy Yard on the Pacific Coast.

"More land duty," she said. "You can refuse it; say you're too sick."

"I can't refuse. It's too important." And he explained: Since the Mexican War the United States stretched from the Atlantic to the Pacific and from Canada to the Rio Grande. There was no Navy Yard on the West Coast, and one was badly needed.

"Read the rest of the letter," he said.

The Navy Yard was to be built on Mare Island in San Pablo Bay near San Francisco. It was important that the work begin as soon as possible.

"You're going to be a busy person," he said. "You'll have to do all the packing. We'll probably be out there four years."

The doctor exploded. "Commander Farragut, you can't possibly leave for San Francisco. You can't even sit up!"

"I can start on a stretcher," Glasgow said. He

grinned. "Don't you doctors prescribe sea voyages for the health?"

"Not around Cape Horn!"

"We'll go by the Nicaraguan Steamship Company. One steamer to the Atlantic port, a river steamer up the San Juan River, a Pacific steamer on the other side. I've seen their advertisements. Comfortable accommodations all the way."

The doctor fumed. Glasgow did not bother to answer.

They left Norfolk in August. Glasgow lay in bed on shipboard, limp as a rag. Virginia sat by him, her eyes dark with worry.

Nine-year-old Loyall roamed all over the ship, talked with the sailors, and reported to his father's cabin three times a day with all the exciting things he had learned. What a little boy he was, Glasgow thought. I wasn't much older when I was Mr. Farragut on the *Essex*!

Glasgow was still flat on his back when they reached Nicaragua. The "comfortable little steamers up the San Juan River" were flat-decked boats with no protection for the passengers but an awning. The passengers huddled on the deck with their luggage piled higgledy-piggledy around them.

The "commodious coaches" to the hotel were flatbed wagons with canvas tops; the "short trip"

199

took all day and far into the night. The "hotel" was a one-room barracks with canvas cots, and a curtain dividing it into quarters for men and women.

When the Pacific steamer arrived there was another jolting ride down to board it.

The captain frowned at the sight of a passenger being carried aboard on a stretcher. "Anything contagious?"

Virginia didn't lose her temper very often, but she did now. She drew herself up till she looked eight feet tall. "There is nothing wrong with the commander," she said, "but a trip in the comfortable, commodious accommodations of the Nicaraguan Steamship Company!"

The captain didn't say any more.

By the time they reached San Francisco, Glasgow was on his feet. "I always said a sea voyage was good for the health!"

Virginia didn't smile. "So far as I'm concerned, I hope I never see another ship for the next two years!"

At Mare Island they found a sloop, the *Warren*, at anchor. It would be the commander's home, a man said, till a house could be built.

Glasgow didn't look toward Virginia. He waited for the explosion. She began to laugh.

In the beginning the workmen on Mare Island eyed their commandant warily, with a "shut-face" look. He was navy, and the navy's first act at Mare Island hadn't made that body popular. It had ordered all houses off Mare Island. Some people had lived there all their lives. Now they had to move.

The workmen lived across the bay in the little town of Vallejo. Boats took them back and forth morning and evening. Glasgow and Virginia entered into the life of the town. Loyall went to school there. But that did not help the way the workmen looked at their commandant.

Glasgow could sense their mood. But the only thing he could do about it was to ignore it and get to work. He waited until other things were well under way before he had a home built for them. Then it was just a little cottage. Someday the commandant of Mare Island would have an impressive home. He could not waste time now being impressive.

He was out of doors most of the time, either walking or riding horseback from one end of the island to the other.

"You may not be at sea," Virginia remarked once, "but you're certainly a man of action."

He laughed and hugged her.

"I've never seen you look so well."

"I've never felt better! Never in my life!"

One evening Loyall came from school, bubbling as usual with things to tell his father. "I wish I

201

could tell you what the men say about you!"

"Why can't you?"

"I'm not supposed to swear."

Startled, Glasgow stared at his son. "The workmen swear about me?"

"Yes, sir! I wish I could tell you! I know what I'll do! I'll say *dash-dash* for swear words! How's that?"

"Go right ahead."

"They say 'Captain Farragut's a *dash-dash* fine man!' and 'Captain Farragut's the *dash-dashest* best navy man I ever had any dealings with!' and 'I'd go through *dash-dash* for that man!'" Loyall beamed. "And all those *dash-dashes* are for different words. I never heard so many words before! They certainly do like you!"

Glasgow hugged him. "Thank you, son."

"But I wish I could tell you what they really say. It sounds a lot more *earnest* with the real words."

"That's all right. I get the idea. It's nice of them to promote me to captain, isn't it?"

"They say you ought to be one. They say 'If that *dash-dash* navy had any sense he'd be a captain!'"

They had been at Mare Island a little over a year when a special letter came; Glasgow was now Captain Farragut. Loyall ran out of the cottage to yell the news at the first man he saw.

At noon a committee of workmen came to call

on Captain Farragut. They had had a meeting. They had talked about stopping work half a day to celebrate. Then they had decided—*dash-dash*—that the way to celebrate was to put in an hour of overtime without pay. And that —*dash-dash*—was just what they were going to do—*dash-dash*!

A visitor came to Mare Island and had dinner with Glasgow and Virginia. He was full of exciting news. The Panama Railroad was done. He had crossed Panama in four hours instead of four days! "Panama was always bad enough," he said, "and if you remember the crossing at Nicaragua—"

"Distinctly!" Virginia said.

After three years the Mare Island Navy Yard could take care of almost any repair a ship needed. There was another year's work to do, but already the fame of the yard was spreading.

"You've been rather happy here, haven't you?" Virginia asked.

"Rather happy? I've been very happy!" Glasgow said.

"Except," she said quietly, "when a ship comes in from a long, long voyage. You smile, but I think you have to work at smiling."

"Yes," he admitted, "I do miss sea duty."

"Maybe when this duty's done, you'll get it."

"Maybe." He mustered a smile. But he did not have much hope.

They had been home in Norfolk only a short

time when orders came. Captain Farragut would command the new screw-sloop *Brooklyn*, first of the four sister ships being built.

When he went aboard the *Brooklyn*, Glasgow knew he had entered a new world. The *Brooklyn* was ship-rigged; she could move under sail. But she also had a screw propeller, 14 feet in diameter, driven by two powerful steam engines. Her smoke stack could be telescoped when she was under sail. When it was raised, it was 50 feet high and 7 feet in diameter.

The sailors cursed the steam engines. Smoke and cinders fouling their decks and sails! They had no place on a proper ship.

The muttering died to a mumble the day the *Brooklyn* was due to sail on a shakedown cruise. In spite of a dead calm she sailed on schedule.

The *Brooklyn*'s first duty was to take Minister McLane to Mexico and to stand by to help him. Years ago Mexico had been in turmoil and Anglos living there had been in danger. History in Mexico was repeating itself. In the navy, Glasgow thought, there would be a difference.

The *Brooklyn* had advantages over the *John Adams*. She would not be becalmed if the wind died; she could not be driven on a lee shore by a contrary wind. But the Gulf of Mexico still had dangers; he would have to watch out for reefs and shoals; the *Brooklyn* drew 16 feet.

Late in 1859 special orders came for the *Brooklyn*. She would carry Minister McLane up the Mississippi to New Orleans and stand by three days for him. Glasgow beamed. A chance to see William and his family! It had been so long—too long.

When the *Brooklyn* stood off New Orleans, Glasgow called for a boat, went ashore, asked directions, and hurried to William's house. As he turned the last corner he was smiling and walking so fast he was almost running.

He rapped on the door and waited, smiling.

A solemn-faced stranger opened it and murmured, "You are a friend of the family?"

Glasgow wrote to Virginia that night. "William is dead. I got here too late to talk to him but in time for the funeral. I tried to comfort his wife. I promised her we would come to New Orleans to see her the first time I had leave."

Late in 1860 Glasgow completed his tour of duty on the *Brooklyn*. He went home to find Norfolk a city in turmoil. The tension between North and South had been growing. It had reached the breaking point. Every morning officers in Norfolk gathered in the back of Daily's store to talk over the latest news.

Southern states were seceding from the Union.

There was talk that Virginia might secede next.

"That's impossible!" Glasgow said. "Virginia is the Mother of Presidents! Four of the first five Presidents from here! Six of the first ten! The state that gave Washington and Jefferson and Madison and Monroe to the nation could not leave the Union!"

Often when Glasgow entered their house he found some of Virginia's family talking with her. A silence would settle over the room when he entered. Then conversation would begin again—very lame conversation, as though people's tongues were talking when their thoughts were somewhere else.

He did not question Virginia. When she wanted to tell him about it, she would.

Finally she said, "They say our state is going to secede."

"Nonsense!" He took hold of her hands. They were cold and shaking. "Please, dear, don't let them upset you."

"I—I—can't help it!" Virginia leaned her head against him and sobbed. "I feel as though my world is being torn in two. Almost all my life has been spent here in Norfolk. Everyone I love—except you—has been born here."

"Virginia won't secede! That I promise you!"

At last she dried her eyes. "All right. I'll stop

stewing about it. When they talk about it, I'll just smile and think of something else!"

"That's my darling!"

But one morning in April of 1861 he stood in Daily's store and stared at his fellow officers. "No, no! I don't believe it! It couldn't happen!"

But it had happened. The State of Virginia had seceded and joined the Confederacy.

"Well, one thing about it, Farragut," one officer said. "You'll be our first admiral in the Confederacy."

"I'm not going to be anything in the Confederacy."

"*What!*"

"I'm staying with the Union."

The officers hammered him from all sides.

"Farragut, don't be a fool!"

"You don't think the North would trust you with a command, do you?"

"You're just throwing away your career!"

"Not a chance that they'd trust you with a command!"

"Born in Tennessee!"

"Your family is in New Orleans. Louisiana's already with the Confederacy!"

"Don't throw away your chance for a career!"

"The South is your home!"

"You've been in Norfolk for years!"

207

"You can't turn against your state!"

"I can—*if my state turns against my nation*!"

An officer spoke through his teeth. "You can't talk that way in Norfolk, Farragut."

"Then I can get out of Norfolk!" He strode away, leaving a silence behind him. He felt cold stares boring into his back.

18. "HANDSOME COFFINS"

When he reached home, three women of Norfolk were at the door, just taking their leave. One spoke to Virginia in a loud, hissing whisper.

"Impossible! I'm sure he won't be a traitor!"

When they had gone he asked, "Who won't be a traitor to what?"

"They say Virginia has seceded. That you won't be a traitor to our state."

"Did they say anything about being a traitor to our nation?" She did not answer. "Dear, more than fifty years ago I took an oath. I swore to defend my country against all enemies. I can't go back on that oath. I'm leaving Norfolk today."

Color drained from her face.

"You don't have to go with me. You may stay

here with your family and friends. I can't decide that for you. I've taken an oath. You haven't."

She was still pale, but her voice was steady. "I made a vow: 'In sickness, in health, for better, for worse . . .' Wherever you go, Loyall and I go too."

They left Norfolk that day. Soon they were in the little village of Hastings-on-the-Hudson above New York City.

Glasgow's heart ached for his wife. Only once before had she been uprooted from Norfolk— when she had gone to Mare Island. That had been a proud leave-taking. Her husband was doing something important for his country. Everybody had kissed her good-bye and wished her luck. There had been no loving wishes in this good-bye. Only her mother had kissed her good-bye, and her mother had wept.

Glasgow wrote the Navy Department, gave them his address, and said he awaited orders. He waited . . . and waited. He paced the house like a caged animal. He went for long walks. Day after day, rain or shine, he tramped the hills until he was tired enough to sleep.

One evening he came in to find Virginia in tears. A neighbor had "thought she ought to know." Everybody knew the Farraguts were Southerners. People suspected that Captain Farragut was an enemy agent of the Confederacy, that he was plotting to destroy the Croton Aqueduct to cut off the water supply to New York City.

He didn't know whether to laugh or swear. He did both; he swore in Spanish.

"I can't stand it!" Virginia sobbed. "We don't belong anywhere! In Norfolk, we're traitors to the South. Up here, we're plotting against the North!"

"Do you want to go back to your family?"

"*What did you say?*" In spite of tears, her eyes blazed.

"Your family will forgive you. They'll welcome you home. All you'll have to do is agree with them that I am a traitor to the state."

She straightened, and dried her tears. "I'm sorry. I won't go to pieces again."

"When they send for me and I'm commanding a ship, people will stop suspecting I'm an enemy agent."

"Do you think they will send for you?"

"Of course! They need every ship, every man, every officer they can lay their hands on!"

"I don't see why," she said. "We're not fighting overseas. Everything is right here inside our own coastline."

"England and France will be ready to help the South. England needs cotton for her mills. France would like to see her flag over New Orleans again.

211

They'll both trade guns and ammunition—any
thing the South needs—for what they want."

"But what can the navy do about it?"

"Blockade the coast. Stop shipments of cotton
going out of the South, stop supplies coming in.
Blockade . . ." He shook his head. "The grimmest,
dullest, most spirit-breaking service in the navy. I
know. I went through it in the Mexican War."

"Will it take all our ships to do it?"

"It'll take twenty times as many ships as we
have." He spread a map. "Look at the coastline of
the South—from Virginia to the tip of Florida and
around the Gulf Coast to the Rio Grande and the
border of Mexico. More than three thousand miles
of coastline. Important ports. Norfolk; Wilmington, North Carolina; Charleston, South Carolina;
Mobile, Alabama; New Orleans; up the Mississippi. Next to New York, New Orleans is the busi-
est port in the nation."

"We'll have to blockade all those ports?"

"All those ports and dozens of places in between. There are more than a hundred and fifty
bayous, rivers, bays, and inlets where shallow-
draft vessels can dart in and out."

Virginia sat in silence, tracing the coastline with
her finger. At last she said, "I wonder why they
don't send for you?"

Had he heard the answer that last day in Norfolk? *"You don't think the Union will trust you with a command, do you?"*

Six months passed before a letter came from the Navy Department. His fingers shook as he opened it. He read it, crushed it, and threw it on the floor. He swore in French, Spanish, Italian, and Arabic.

"What's wrong?" Virginia asked.

"I'm to sit on a Retiring Board in Brooklyn. Sit with a lot of old fuddy-duddies and decide how many other fuddy-duddies we should retire!"

"What will you do?" she asked.

"Obey orders!" he snapped. Then he bent to kiss her. "I'm sorry. Forgive me, dear."

In Brooklyn he heard talk of the ironclad ship that John Ericsson was building for the Union. Opinions clashed:

"Revolutionary! The ship of tomorrow!"

"Ugliest thing you ever saw! Not a proper ship at all!"

"Cheesebox on a raft!"

"Impregnable against any naval gun in the world!"

"I wouldn't serve on her for a million dollars!"

Glasgow went to see the ironclad. He stared at it, speechless. He had never imagined anything so ugly. No towering sides, no proud sails, no broadsides of guns. Just a flat deck and a turret.

The turret, Ericsson explained, would have two

guns—eleven-inch Dahlgrens. A single shot could sink any wooden ship afloat. The turret revolved so the guns could be fired in any direction. "An advantage over the guns in broadside," Ericsson said. "You've heard the saying that a standard ship is like a shark? The shark must turn belly-up to bite; the ship must turn her side to the enemy to bring her guns to bear."

Glasgow did not answer; he was trying to keep his face blank to hide his disgust.

John Ericsson was not fooled. "No, Captain Farragut. It doesn't look like 'a proud ship,' does it? It's not a proud ship! It's a floating battery! I grant you a ship in full sail is a beautiful sight. But remember this, sir! Send boys against ironclads in wooden ships, and you send them to their death! Your beautiful ships will make very handsome coffins!" Ericsson strode away, leaving Glasgow staring at the "cheesebox on a raft."

He had been sitting on the Retiring Board for long, dreary weeks when he got a letter from Commander David Dixon Porter. Mr. Porter had just arrived from Washington; he had a message for Captain Farragut; he'd call on the captain the next evening.

Little David Dixon . . . Glasgow counted up. Good heavens! Little David Dixon was in his forties! Did he still look so much like his father?

The commander wore a luxuriant black beard. His message, he said, was more in the nature of a question. "Are you ready, Captain Farragut, in spite of your ties with the South, to fight for the Union?"

"I am!"

"To lead a fleet on a difficult and dangerous mission?"

"I am ready for any duty my country asks of me."

"Thank you, sir." The commander got up. "I wish I could say more, but I can't."

Glasgow did not sleep very soundly until after his first interview with the Navy Department in Washington. Assistant Secretary Fox talked with him.

"Your post will be in the Gulf of Mexico. You will relieve Captain McKean and take over the West Gulf Blockading Squadron." Mr. Fox spread a chart. "Everything from Pensacola to the Rio Grande will be under your command."

Blockade duty? Was that all? Glasgow waited.

"Your real objective—which no one must suspect until you strike—will be to capture New Orleans."

At last! Something to do!

"Getting up the Mississippi to New Orleans presents some problems."

215

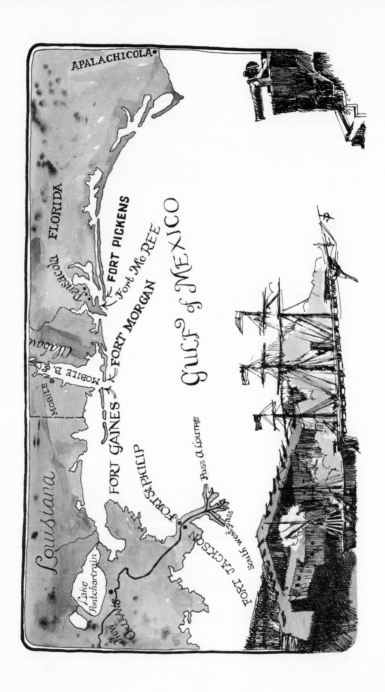

"I know," Glasgow said. "Two of the 'problems' are named Fort Jackson and Fort St. Philip."

"Most men we've consulted say it's impossible for wooden ships to pass the forts. Mr. Porter has a plan: A squadron of mortar boats will enter the river and bombard the forts. He says he can reduce the forts in forty-eight hours. We've ordered mortars and shells; we're strengthening some schooners to bear the concussion of the mortars."

"I doubt if he can reduce the forts in forty-eight hours. I saw the action off San Juan in 'thirty-eight. The French tried mortar fire. It didn't have much effect."

"You don't approve of the mortars?"

"I don't think mortar fire will reduce the forts—in two days—or even in four. The delay, waiting on mortar fire, will just give the enemy more time to get ready for us. The minute we enter the Mississippi they'll know we are going to try to take New Orleans. The sooner we can run past the forts the better. But since you've planned to try the mortars, I'll go along with the plan. Give them a chance to show what they can do." He added to himself, *or what they can't do.*

Mr. Fox let it go at that and talked of other things. Washington was worried, he said, about an ironclad the South was building. When the North had surrendered Norfolk Navy Yard, they had

217

tried to destroy the *Merrimac*. But she sank before she burned. The South had hauled her out of the water, cut her down to a razee, and were making an ironclad ram of her. She had a heavy iron-plated ram out from her bow, and her sides were plated with iron. The North had five ships on guard in Hampton Roads. They hoped to keep the *Merrimac* from getting out to sea. Ericsson's little *Monitor* was behind schedule.

"Yes," Glasgow said, "I heard the government had failed to meet its promised payments. Ericsson and his partners are too low on funds to hire all-night shifts to speed the work."

Mr. Fox didn't answer that. He only shrugged. Even if the *Monitor* were ready, what could a little vessel like that do against the *Merrimac*?

Glasgow didn't say what he was thinking—that he hoped to heaven he'd never have to have anything to do with such a misbegotten freak as that "cheesebox on a raft"!

He went to see his flagship, the *Hartford*. At least, he thought, she looked like a proper ship. She was a sister-ship of the *Brooklyn*, ship-rigged, but carrying two powerful engines, a huge propeller, and a tall telescoping smokestack.

In February of 1862, Flag-Officer Farragut took charge at Ship Island, the base of the West Gulf Blockading Squadron, and began to call in his ships. The island, south of Biloxi, was nearer to Mobile Bay than to New Orleans. That was good. The South would not suspect his destination until he entered the Mississippi.

The Mississippi . . . he thought of the tons of silt that came down the muddy river and settled on the bars across the passes. According to reports, the river carried 19 feet of water over the two deepest passes. But that was in peacetime when traffic was heavy. What about now, since the North had been blockading the passes?

He sent leadsmen to sound the two deepest passes. They reported back cheerfully. Yes, the passes were silted up a bit, but they ought to have no trouble in either of those passes. Southwest Pass was deeper, but Pass à L'Outre, to the east, was nearer Ship Island.

On March 10, Flag-Officer Farragut stood off Pass à L'Outre. It was later than he had expected. It had taken time to call in all his ships and put them in fighting trim. But if everything moved along now, he'd not waste any more time. Two days to get his ships to the head of the passes, four days to wait on that mortar bombardment—that could not reduce those forts to rubble—then the dash past the forts to take New Orleans. He ought to make it by March 20 at the latest.

He ordered the *Brooklyn* to lead the way over

LAKE PONTCHARTRAIN

CAT IS.

CHANDELEUR SOUND

NEW ORLEANS

LAKE BORGNE

CHANDELEUR ISLANDS

CARROLLTON

JACKSON
VERSAILLES

LAFAYETTE
ALGIERS

L. CATOUACHA

MISSISSIPPI RIVER

L. QUACHA

MISSISSIPPI RIVER

BLACK B.

L. QUITMAN

Ft. St. PHILIP
Ft. JACKSON

BARATARIA
BAY

B. RONDE

PASS A L'OUTRE

GRAND PASS

BLIND B.
N.E. PASS

GRAND I.

S.E. PASS

TIMBALIER B.
TIMBALIER GRAND PASS

EAST B.

S.W. PASS

DELTA of the MISSISSIPPI

GULF OF MEXICO

the bar, since she drew only 16 feet . . . but the *Brooklyn* went aground. For three days they tried to drag her over the bar. It was hopeless. The Mississippi was still a devil. Her muddy bottom had fooled his leadsmen who were used to sounding offshore and in salt water.

Three days wasted. By the time they had hauled the *Brooklyn* off and sailed around to the Southwest Pass more time had been wasted. New Orleans by March 20? He'd do well to be at the head of the passes by then! He got the *Brooklyn* and the *Hartford* over. Now for the deeper-draft vessels . . . It was even worse than he feared: two days to get one over, three days for another. After ten days' struggle, they dragged the side-wheeler *Mississippi* over; the *Pensacola* was still aground.

Glasgow was on a gunboat, watching the struggle with the *Pensacola* when an officer, white-faced, came aboard the gunboat and thrust a New Orleans newspaper into his hand.

The South was wildly cheering the triumph of the ironclad *Merrimac*. On March 8, she had steamed out of her berth to meet the five Union ships at Hampton Roads. One smashing blow of the ironclad ram and the *Cumberland* sank. She had gone down with all guns blazing, but the shot had rattled off the sloping casemates of the *Merrimac*.

221

Then the ironclad had turned on the *Cumberland* and set her afire with red-hot shot. She had burned and blown up.

The other three Union ships had tried to come to the aid of the two and had gone aground. The ebbing tide had sent the *Merrimac* back to her berth; that same ebbing tide had driven the three deep-draft Union ships even deeper in the mud. Tomorrow the *Merrimac* would complete her conquest! She would destroy the other three wooden ships, then go up the Potomac and take Washington!

Five proud ships helpless before an ironclad! Ericsson's words hammered in Glasgow's mind: *"Your beautiful wooden ships will make handsome coffins."*

19. TRIUMPH AND DISASTER

News of the *Merrimac* stunned Glasgow's captains. News about the defenses of New Orleans did not make them feel any better. The South had one ironclad ram, the *Manassas*, already in the Mississippi. Another, the *Louisiana*, more powerful than the *Merrimac*, was almost ready for action.

And we must waste time with the mortars! Glasgow said to himself.

The South had a squadron of other gunboats waiting in the river above the forts. What was worse they had a massive barricade across the river, just below the forts. It was made of huge logs—four and five feet in diameter—and derelict schooners, all fastened together with heavy chains. The barricade would block the way and hold the Union ships helpless under the guns of Fort Jackson. Even when the mortars reduced the forts . . .

And when the mortars can't reduce the forts? When I order our wooden ships to run past the forts—what then? He did not say what he was thinking.

On April 18, the mortars opened fire. A hollow roar, then a hissing *whoosh*, and a thirteen-inch shell arched into the sky trailing a burning fuse, fell, and exploded. The captain watched and

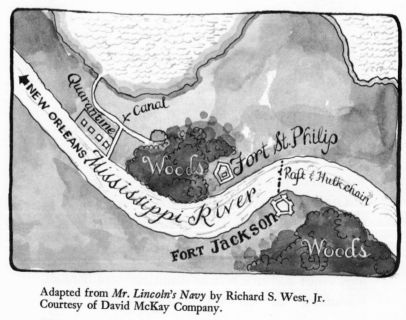

Adapted from *Mr. Lincoln's Navy* by Richard S. West, Jr. Courtesy of David McKay Company.

looked more cheerful. Forty-eight hours, Commander Porter had said, would reduce the forts.

But forty-eight hours passed, and the guns of the forts were still booming. Glasgow called his captains together. He would give the mortars a little more time. But if they could not reduce the forts, he would run past them and take New Orleans. When New Orleans fell, the forts would fall. Their supplies would be cut off.

His captains were appalled. They were polite— they had to be—but they argued long and hard. Had the flag-officer considered . . . Didn't the flag-officer think . . .

What they would really like to say, Glasgow told himself, is "You hare-brained, reckless fool!" He let them say their say. Then he got up. "Thank you, gentlemen. I'll dictate my sailing orders. You'll all have copies. When the time comes the signal will be two vertical red lanterns. Tonight we'll break the barricade."

At nine that night Captain Bell came to his flag-officer's cabin. He was taking the *Itasca* and the *Pinola* up to break the barricade. Everything was in order. While the gunboats were on their mission the mortars would loose a heavy barrage; they'd keep the forts too busy for the gunners to notice the boats at the barricade. ". . . we hope," Captain Bell added, smiling. He started out, then

225

turned and laid a letter on the table. "Flag-Officer, will you see that this is delivered—just in case?"

Glasgow's scalp prickled. He took the letter, shook hands with his captain, and went to the deck with him. He stood there as the gunboats prowled off into the night. They showed no lights. There was no sound but the throb of their engines. The mortars loosed a barrage. At each hollow roar a comet streaked into the sky.

Glasgow went back to his cabin. He'd be a fool to stay on deck waiting for the return of Captain Bell. He ought to get some work done. But he had been pacing the deck for an hour before Captain Bell reported back. "Mission accomplished, Flag-Officer. No casualties."

Limp with relief, Glasgow went back to the work he had intended to do. He wakened three hours later, his head on his arm.

The next day an officer reported from General Butler's troops. They were on the east bank above the forts. When the forts fell they would take possession. "And, Flag-Officer!" The man was so excited he almost stuttered. "News from Hampton Roads, sir. You heard what happened March 8? When the *Merrimac* sank two of our ships? Well, the next morning, sir, she came out again to destroy the other three. They were all aground and helpless. But Ericsson's little *Monitor* had got

226

there in the night. That little *Monitor*! Only seven hundred tons and two guns! But she fought the *Merrimac* to a draw, sent her limping back to her berth, saved the Union ships, and didn't lose a man!"

After the officer had gone, Glasgow sat a long time in his cabin, staring at nothing. Shallow-draft, turreted so her guns could sweep the horizon . . . Was that monstrosity "the fighting ship of tomorrow"?

For six days the mortars roared—and the guns of the forts roared back. April 23, a deserter brought grim news. The *Louisiana* was almost ready for action.

Glasgow called his captains together. They were going past the forts in the morning. Moonrise would be at three thirty. They would weigh anchor at two o'clock. That would give them time to ghost past the forts in darkness.

The captains said, "Aye, aye, sir." They looked what they could not say.

At two A.M. the vertical red lanterns gave the signal. "Get under way!"

Glasgow was on deck. As soon as all the vessels had signaled that they were ready . . .

The Mississippi mud had upset their schedule of getting over the bar; now it upset their schedule of weighing anchors. It was after three A.M. before

227

all the ships were under way. The first vessel was just going through the barricade when the moon rose, silhouetting her against the night.

The guns of the forts roared; fire rafts blazed. Soon the whole river was lighted, revealing the Union fleet to the Confederate gunners. Then as the ships came alongside the forts and loosed their broadsides a pall of flame-slashed smoke hung over them.

The *Hartford* had just gone through the barricade when a fire raft bore down on her. The helmsmen swerved the ship to escape the raft and went too far to starboard. A jolt sent men sprawling on the deck. The *Hartford* was aground, right under the guns of Fort St. Philip. A Confederate tugboat shoved the fire raft against her port side, and the *Hartford* was ablaze to the tops of her masts.

Some of the crew panicked; they deserted their posts and grabbed up gratings, ready to jump overboard. But their flag-officer, flanked by his captains, came stalking down the deck as calmly as though on dress parade. The bosun's pipe shrilled the signal for fire stations. Men dropped the gratings and grabbed fire hoses.

Glasgow saw Signalman Osbon kneeling on the port side of the *Hartford*, his coat pulled over his head. "Come, come, Mr. Osbon! This is no time for prayers!"

Mr. Osbon looked out from under his coat. "Flag-Officer, just stand by a minute, and you'll see the quickest answer to prayer you ever saw!" He had removed the caps from three shells. Now he dumped them overboard onto the fire raft. They exploded, tearing a great hole in the raft. Her fire guttered and died as she sank.

"Well done, sir!"

"Thank you, Flag-Officer."

The fire crews had put out the fire on the *Hartford*, but she was still aground.

Captain Wainwright sent for an engineer. Was he doing everything he could to pull the *Hartford* off?

The throttles were wide open, the engineer said. The only other thing he could do was reduce the water in the boilers. But that was dangerous— mighty dangerous.

"If we don't get off, it's fatal!" Captain Wainwright said.

"Aye, aye, sir!" The engineer went below.

Soon the pounding of the engines shook the deck until men could hardly keep their feet. When the *Hartford* backed off the mud bank Glasgow realized he had been holding his breath until his chest ached.

By dawn the Union ships were safely above the forts. All the Confederate gunboats had either fled or been sunk. The *Louisiana*—thank heaven—had not been ready for action. The wooden ships had done what men thought was impossible: They had passed between two powerful forts in spite of fire rafts and enemy gunboats, a barricade and the river.

The river, Glasgow thought, was the worst of it!

By April 29, the job was done. The Union had paid a fearful price in battered ships, in dead and wounded men, but Flag-Officer Farragut could report "mission accomplished." New Orleans had fallen; the forts had fallen; General Butler was in charge.

Glasgow stopped writing his report and sat grim-faced. His orders were to go north, rendezvous with the river squadron, and capture Vicksburg. A silly business! River gunboats built for that warfare were on their way down. Why not leave that job to boats built for it? Why risk his deep-draft vessels up the Mississippi? But orders were orders. Unless he could hammer some facts into heads back in Washington . . .

His next objective, he wrote, should be Mobile Bay. Next to New Orleans, Mobile was the largest port on the Gulf. If the army could furnish five thousand men to attack Fort Morgan from the land side, Mobile Bay could be taken. The sooner the better, before the South had time to strengthen their defenses.

Meantime he would follow orders. He had sent the gunboats ahead. As soon as the bigger vessels were in trim he would start up with them. He doubted if his deep-draft vessels would be safe very far up the river. The Mississippi was high now, but it was past the time of spring floods. When the river started falling, the ocean-going ships could be stranded.

When the *Hartford* was ready, she went crawling up the river, her leadsmen sounding constantly. In spite of their care she went aground. It took two days to lighten her of everything that could be taken off before she floated again. Glasgow put more leadsmen in the chains and the *Hartford* crawled upriver even more slowly.

At last he joined his gunboats below Vicksburg. His captains were grim. Every boat had been aground; the river had taken a toll in damaged hulls and lost anchors. The river, they said, was worse than the enemy!

"I know," Glasgow said. "What about Vicksburg?"

A naval force acting alone could never take Vicksburg, his captains said. The city was too high above the river for their guns to do much damage. Only an army—and a big one at that—on the high land behind Vicksburg could ever compel her to surrender.

Glasgow reconnoitered and had to agree with his captains. The trip to Vicksburg had been a wild-goose chase. He left some gunboats on blockade duty and took his deep-draft vessels back to New Orleans.

A stack of letters awaited him.

He groaned, slumped in his chair, closed his eyes, and told his secretary "Start reading."

The first two letters praised his "magnificent accomplishment" in capturing New Orleans. That was the end of praise. The other letters grew more and more stern. Flag-Officer Farragut would forget about Mobile Bay! He would obey orders! He would rendezvous with the River Squadron and Halleck's army. He would take Vicksburg!

Once more he made the inch-by-inch trip up the Mississippi. This time he even passed Vicksburg. Not that it meant anything. He did not silence the guns of Vicksburg.

Above the city he waited for the River Squadron and the army—waited while heat and fever took their toll and his men sickened and died.

Flag-Officer Davis finally arrived with his river boats, but no troops came. General Halleck wrote it would be "several weeks" before he could send troops. How much longer, Glasgow wondered,

must he risk his deep-draft vessels so far up the Mississippi? He wrote again to Washington. With fires banked to conserve their coal the two squadrons stood by.

On July 13, a deserter brought word to Flag-Officer Farragut. A powerful ironclad ram, the *Arkansas*, had been built in the Yazoo River above Vicksburg. She was almost ready for action.

"I doubt it," Glasgow said. "These Confederate ironclads are always 'ready for action' about four months before they can bring a gun to bear."

He sent three boats up the Yazoo to check on the *Arkansas*. Hours before they expected word from the boats two of them came steaming back with the *Arkansas* in pursuit. She *was* ready for action!

In vain the Union squadrons beat to quarters. Not a vessel had up enough steam to get under way. They could not maneuver to bring their broadsides to bear on the *Arkansas*. What shot they could pour onto the ironclad rattled off her sloping casemates.

The *Arkansas* ran the gantlet of the Union squadrons, pouring shot into the vessels as she passed. She reached Vicksburg and anchored under the protection of the shore batteries. The Union forces could hear the wild cheering that welcomed the ironclad.

One ironclad had defied two Union squadrons. The Union forces counted the cost: ten men missing, fifty wounded, and eighteen dead.

"If you send wooden ships against ironclads," Ericsson had said, "your beautiful wooden ships will make handsome coffins."

20. "TRAPPED BETWEEN ENEMY FORCES"

Glasgow did not mince matters when he wrote to Secretary Welles. He admitted his mistake:

> *It is with deep mortification that I announce to the Department that, notwithstanding my predictions to the contrary, the ironclad* Arkansas *has at length made her appearance and took us all by surprise....*

He had just sent off that letter when orders came from Washington. Evidently Welles had wakened to the danger of leaving deep-draft ships upriver too long. Flag-Officer Davis would maintain the blockade at Vicksburg; Flag-Officer Farragut would return to his blockade in the Gulf.

Glasgow felt both relief and regret: relief to get

his ships back to the Gulf, regret that he must leave the *Arkansas* to be dealt with by Davis's squadron.

With sick and disheartened men the *Hartford* reached New Orleans. General Butler's troops saluted her with fifteen guns. What, someone muttered, was there to cheer about?

A smiling officer came aboard the *Hartford*. If Flag-Officer Farragut, sir, would call a general muster . . .

When the men were all topside, the officer held out a letter. "For you to read to your men, Flag-Officer."

Congress had voted to establish a new rank in the navy. Flag-Officer Farragut was now Rear-Admiral Farragut.

In the midst of the cheers Glasgow said to himself, I'd give my admiral's stripes to have taken the *Arkansas*!

Back in the Gulf again, his spirits rose. Once more he was off soundings where a proper ship belonged. True, he had a frustrating job to do: one thousand miles of coastline to blockade without enough ships to maintain the watch.

He wrote again to Secretary Welles about the importance of taking Mobile Bay. But news from the North was bad: The Union could not spare troops or ships to help him.

237

News from Vicksburg was bad too. Time and again Union forces tried—and failed—to take the city.

By the spring of 1863 there had been shake-ups in the command of Union forces in the West. General Grant commanded the army; David Dixon Porter, jumped in rank to Acting Rear-Admiral Porter, commanded the River Squadron; General Banks had replaced General Butler at New Orleans.

Meantime the South had strengthened its hold on the Mississippi: heavier guns and more troops at Vicksburg, powerful batteries at Port Hudson. Until those two cities were in Union hands . . .

Glasgow studied a map and traced the course of Red River—entering the Mississippi between Vicksburg and Port Hudson, bringing a constant flow of supplies from Texas to both Confederate strongholds. If he could blockade the mouth of Red River and cut off those supplies . . .

His captains had been shocked when he had run past Forts Jackson and St. Philip to take New Orleans. If New Orleans did not fall, they had said, he would be "trapped between enemy forces." If he ran past Port Hudson to blockade Red River, he would be between enemy forces, and no doubt about it! But if he could cut off supplies . . .

He called his captains together and outlined his

plan. He would take three screw-sloops and the *Mississippi*. Each screw-sloop would have a gunboat lashed to her port side. The ship would protect the gunboat from the guns of Port Hudson. The formation would cut the time of passing the batteries. Speed was going to be important. The South had had a long time to build up its strength.

He explained; he listened to their arguments; he got up, smiled, dismissed them, and dictated his orders.

It was a still dark night on March 14 when the squadron started past Port Hudson—a very dark night. But a Confederate sentry must have had cat eyes and bat ears. A signal rocket flared; huge bonfires blazed across the river, silhouetting the Union ships. The batteries of Port Hudson roared, pouring down a plunging fire on the *Hartford*. It seemed to be forever before she could bring her broadside to bear.

At last her guns roared, and soon a pall of smoke hung over her. The pilot called down from his perch in the mizzen top. He could not see the channel for the smoke. The *Hartford* stopped firing long enough for the smoke to clear. Not a moment too soon! The pilot shouted a warning. The current was carrying them onto the east bank. They were going aground!

Glasgow dashed to the port side, yelling down

to the gunboat, "Back! Back the *Albatross!*"

The instant maneuver swung the *Hartford* about. She reached midchannel again. Once more her guns roared, until she was beyond the batteries of Port Hudson. That bombardment, Glasgow knew, had been the heaviest he had faced since the loss of the *Essex*. The *Hartford* cast loose the *Albatross*. They came to anchor and waited for the rest of the squadron . . . and waited.

What had happened?

Long after they knew it wasn't any use to hope that the others would get through, the men on the *Hartford* stared into the black night.

After a time, below Port Hudson a glare lighted the sky. One of their ships was burning! Presently one *boom* after another told them the fires had reached a gun. Then the fire reached a magazine. A thunderous roar seemed to shake the earth. Then there was silence—silence and the black night.

For a long time Glasgow lay awake facing the grim truth. One ship burned, four ships too disabled to pass Port Hudson. The *Hartford* and the *Albatross* were alone. His captains had thought him reckless enough to be "trapped between enemy forces" with seven vessels. Now he had only two.

He remembered a day more than fifty years ago

when a very small midshipman had stared bewildered at his captain. For his captain had been sitting with bowed head, admitting the dangers he faced. Then his captain had shrugged off his feelings and met his crew with an air of brisk confidence.

The next morning Admiral Farragut faced his men the same way. First, he said, they would run down toward Port Hudson, fire signal guns, and see if they could establish contact with the other ships.

His solemn-faced men said, "Aye, aye, sir." They followed orders; they fired signal guns. No answer. Faces were even more solemn.

"So," their admiral said, "we'll do what we set out to do—blockade Red River! When Grant lays siege to Vicksburg and Banks lays siege to Port Hudson, Red River supplies will be vital to the South. Those Confederate forces will have to tighten their belts!"

He sent a boat upriver to explain the situation to Grant and Porter. If they could send down a gunboat or so, it would help; if they could float down a barge or two of coal, it would help even more. Meantime he would blockade Red River supplies.

A captured Confederate paper headlined news of the Union disaster. Four vessels too disabled to

241

pass Port Hudson! The *Mississippi* aground and burned by her crew! Admiral Farragut trapped! He would soon be a prisoner!

He only smiled. "They'll find they have a bear by the tail!"

The smiles that answered his were a little strained.

A barge of coal floated down to them. Good! They could get fuel. Red River would supply their food!

The blockade began. They captured supply ships and barges, took what they could use, paroled the crews, and sank the vessels. They found a huge store of provisions waiting on a levee. Those went to the bottom too.

Young Colonel Ellet came down to them with one of the river rams of the army—the *Switzerland*. "Admiral Farragut," he asked, "you know the superstition about the salamander? That it can go through fire and live? Well, you have a nickname now, sir. 'The Old Salamander.' I don't agree with the 'Old.' You're the youngest 'old' man I ever saw."

"I'll be sixty-two in July," Glasgow told him. "I always turn a handspring on my birthday. When I can't do that, I'll admit I'm getting old."

They laughed together. But to himself Glasgow admitted that sometimes he did feel old. The two years since the war began had been enough to age any man: the shock of seeing his nation split by war, the heartbreak of uprooting his family from Norfolk, the long wait for a chance to serve his country . . .

For two brief times in the whole two years he had had a chance to do what he believed in: He had captured New Orleans; he was blockading Red River. But otherwise the last two years had been enough to age a man ten years. Now—according to the newspaper—he was trapped.

He had no illusions about the risks he ran. He kept picket boats out night and day to warn him of any attempt to overpower him. No man ever undressed except to change clothes. They all turned in "all standing." At the first warning signal they were at their stations on the double.

Three weeks passed. No word from General Banks laying siege to Port Hudson, no word from the rest of his squadron. How could he get word through? The batteries of Port Hudson covered the river; troops patrolled both sides of it.

One morning his secretary, Mr. Gabaudin, asked, "Admiral Farragut, have you a minute, sir?"

"All the time in the world!"

Mr. Gabaudin pointed to a brush-covered log floating down the river. "Sir, I believe I can get past Port Hudson. I can lie in the bottom of a dugout, covered with debris to look like a floating log. I can reach our ships and get word to General Banks."

"You're volunteering for the mission?"

"I'm begging for it, sir!"

They made their plan. Gabaudin would lie in the bottom of a dugout, with dispatches, a paddle, a revolver, and two rockets. If the dugout grounded on a sandbar, the paddle would help him off—maybe; if sentries discovered him, the revolver would help him escape—maybe; the rockets would signal that he had passed Port Hudson—if he did.

Mr. Gabaudin smiled as he got ready to embark. "Don't worry if I'm longer than you think I'll be, sir. The current may carry me every whichaway!" He raised his hand in salute, then held out a letter. "Sir, would you have this delivered—just in case?"

Glasgow did not pretend to do anything but wait. Hour after hour he stayed on deck, staring into the night. Just before dawn two rockets streaked through the sky. Gabaudin had made it!

The *Hartford* and the *Richmond* made a rendezvous, signaling across a point of land. The *Richmond* reported the damage and the casualties. The signalman also reported: "New Orleans is worried about Admiral Farragut. They have heard he is a prisoner, or even dead."

"Tell them I'm very much alive and intend to stay that way!"

Early in May the Union gunboat *Arizona* reached them. She had come up the Atchafalaya River. The Confederates had retreated from it. So Admiral Farragut's squadron had a new route for supplies and a "back door" to reach New Orleans.

Glasgow knew by the sudden weariness that hit him what the last seven weeks had meant. "One thing about it," he said to himself, "this blockade has not been dull."

Soon news came down the Mississippi. Porter had ferried Grant's troops across the river, landing them below Vicksburg. Porter had orders to take over the patrol of the Mississippi and to let Rear-Admiral Farragut return to his command in the Gulf.

Eight weeks after Confederate newspapers had headlined "Admiral Farragut Trapped!" the newsboys in New Orleans were shouting an extra: "Admiral Farragut Alive! Admiral Farragut in New Orleans!" They even had a new nickname for him: "The Game Cock."

On July 4, Vicksburg surrendered; on July 9, Port Hudson fell. The whole of the Mississippi was in Union hands. Texas could no longer be the granary of the Confederacy.

New orders from Washington: Admiral Farragut would report home on furlough; he would bring the screw-sloops *Hartford*, *Richmond*, and *Brooklyn* north for a complete overhaul.

And I can do with a complete overhaul myself, he thought. He would be home in Hastings in time to see Loyall off to enter West Point. The army instead of the navy. That was a bit of a disappointment. Glasgow had written President Lincoln asking for an appointment to Annapolis for Loyall. No answer. Perhaps President Lincoln had never gotten the letter. Well, at least his son would be in the service of his country. And he'd be home in time to see his lad off to the academy. Home . . . Just to sit still and rest!

But when the *Hartford* came to anchor he found that New York was not going to let him "sit still and rest." Admiral Farragut had to be "honored" with one affair after another. And New York in August was hotter than New Orleans had been.

At last he and Virginia were in Hastings together. Sometimes they talked; sometimes they just sat and smiled at each other.

"Will it take long to repair the *Hartford*?" she asked.

"Hard to tell, dear. She was hit two hundred and forty times. And—"

Virginia gasped. He decided not to go into detail.

Autumn passed; winter came; still the *Hartford* was not ready for action. December began.

"Loyall will be home for Christmas," Virginia said. "Wouldn't it be wonderful if we could have Christmas together?"

"Yes, dear. Wonderful!"

But news from Mobile Bay was worrying Glasgow. The South was building their biggest ironclad ram above Mobile—the *Tennessee*. If they got her done and down into the bay, his wooden ships would need help. I never thought the day would come, he said to himself, but I'll be asking for a monitor!

In Washington he had talked to Secretary Welles. He had hammered home the facts: He needed swifter, more shoal-draft vessels to catch the Confederate blockade-runners. Above all he needed to take Mobile Bay! Enough troops to attack Fort Morgan on the landside, an ironclad to oppose the *Tennessee* if she got down into the bay. Secretary Welles had promised to do his best. He hadn't promised what his best would be or when he'd do it.

In January the *Hartford* sailed in a snowstorm. Soon she was back in the sweltering heat of the Gulf. Back on the spirit-breaking duty of blockade without the vessels needed to do the job. February ... March ... April ... Still no troops, no ironclad.

247

Word about the *Tennessee*. She was launched! They would have to tow her down and raise her to get her over Dog River Bar, then load her with her coal, guns, and ammunition.

Glasgow walked the deck. If only he could have one monitor to attack her while she was helpless on the bar! But he did not. By the end of May the *Tennessee* was in Mobile Bay, ready for action. Ready, the Southern papers said, to come out of the bay, destroy Admiral Farragut's wooden fleet, run up to New Orleans, and restore that proud city to the Confederacy!

21. "DAMN THE TORPEDOES!"

Glasgow rushed off a letter to Washington with news of the *Tennessee*. Maybe now he'd get the troops and the ironclads he needed. Meantime, until help came he'd have to face the threat of the *Tennessee* with nothing but his wooden ships.

He did some sitting with his head in his hands, but he did it when he was alone. When he called his captains together, he said nothing of possible defeat. He outlined exactly how they'd sink the *Tennessee*.

His captains said, "Yes, Admiral Farragut." Their eyes said the rest of what they were thinking. *"We haven't a chance!"*

The long vigil began. Days and nights inched by. Weeks passed. June ended.

At last, word from Washington: Four monitors

were on their way to help him, two from New York and two from the Mississippi. Word from New Orleans too: Troops were coming.

Finally! He could enter Mobile Bay!

Confederate papers and his own reconnoitering had kept him posted on what he would face when he entered Mobile Bay. Fort Morgan, the papers said, was impregnable, armed to the hilt with more guns and heavier ones, manned with almost one thousand men, and provisioned to stand a siege of six months.

An enemy ship trying to enter Mobile Bay would have to come directly under the guns of Fort Morgan. The channel between Fort Gaines and Fort Morgan had always been narrow. Now they had narrowed it even more. A row of pilings blocked the western side near Fort Gaines; beyond the pilings toward Fort Morgan, a row of buoys marked where they had placed torpedoes—mines floating under water, set to explode on contact. One torpedo could sink any ship afloat. An enemy ship entering Mobile Bay could choose her path to destruction—over the torpedoes or under the guns of Fort Morgan.

Glasgow had the ship's carpenter carve some little blocks to represent his vessels: the four monitors, the seven ships, and the seven gunboats. Then on a table marked with the points of the

250

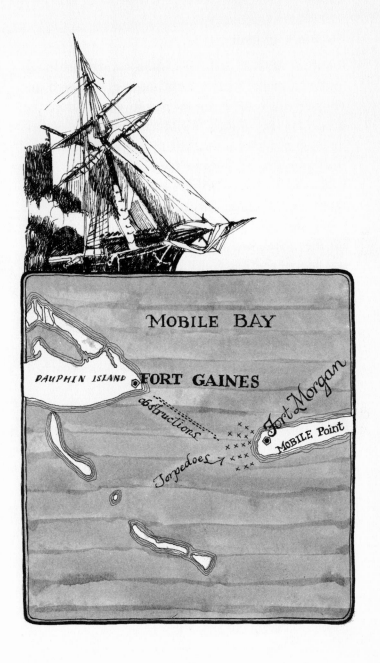

MOBILE BAY

DAUPHIN ISLAND **FORT GAINES**

Fort Morgan

MOBILE Point

obstructions

Torpedoes

compass he outlined Fort Morgan, the channel, and the place of the torpedoes. He plotted his course: the four monitors to the east nearest the guns of Fort Morgan; his seven ships midchannel, each with a gunboat lashed to her port side, as he had passed Port Hudson. He smiled wryly. As he had *tried* to pass Port Hudson. Of seven vessels only two had gotten through.

He shrugged off that memory. No use thinking of the possibility of failure; a commander who considered the possibility of defeat was half licked already.

What he must plan was the way to victory. So he plotted each step of the way: the position of each vessel, the distances between them, their speed, the compass bearing as they approached Fort Morgan and as they passed it.

The fleet would go in early in the morning on flood tide. Then even if one of his ships were disabled, the gunboat lashed to her side could carry her through. With luck he would go in when the wind was from the southwest. That would blow the smoke of battle into the eyes of the gunners of Fort Morgan.

As always he dictated orders for his captains:

Strip your vessels and prepare for combat. Send down all spare spars and rigging. Put splinter nets on the starboard side. Barricade

*wheel and steersmen with sails and ham-
mocks. Lay chains or sandbags over machinery on deck to resist plunging fire. Hang
sheet chains over the sides to prevent hulling.
Land your starboard boats, or lower them
and tow them on the port side. Lower the
port boats to the water's edge. Place leadsman and pilot in the port quarter boat. . . .*

July ended. Two of the monitors, the *Manhattan*
from New York and the *Chickasaw* from New Orleans, arrived just ahead of a threatening storm
and found safe anchorage. The storm came—not
quite a hurricane but severe enough.

"If a monitor's out in this," an officer said,
"scratch one ironclad."

But the monitor *Winnebago* came in through
the storm and reported all snug. Strange craft
those monitors!

The last of the four, the *Tecumseh*, had reached
Pensacola but needed repairs. Glasgow sent two
vessels over to hurry her along, then ordered a
boat and went to call on the captains of the monitors standing by.

On the *Chickasaw* men stripped to the waist
were working on the flat deck between the double
turrets. One glanced at Glasgow, took a second
look, then yelled, "Oh, Lord! The Admiral! Somebody *do* something!"

"At ease," Glasgow said. "I just came to see how you're getting along."

They took him below to the engine room. More men, stripped to the waist and smoke-begrimed, were working with an engine.

A boy with a tousle of hair and a big grin looked up from the engine and saluted. "Welcome aboard, Admiral Farragut, sir! I'm Captain Perkins. I was just giving a hand with this engine. I like machinery. Am I glad, sir, that we got here in time to fight with you! I've read everything about you since—" He stopped. "I talk too much."

"People say I talk too much too," Glasgow told him. "Of course they just say it behind my back." He laughed with the young captain. "How old are you?"

"Twenty-seven, sir!"

He toured the *Chickasaw* with Captain Perkins; he agreed with everything the young man said in praise of her. He kept his memories of frigates and clouds of white sails to himself.

"Come and see me on the *Hartford*," he said.

Another grin, even wider this time. "Yes, sir! I'll come with all my clothes on!"

Glasgow returned to the *Hartford*, cheered by his visit with his youngest captain.

He sent word to Pensacola. He could not wait much longer on the *Tecumseh*. He would enter Mobile Bay the morning of August 5.

The afternoon of August 4, he called his captains together for one last briefing. Captain Perkins was there "with all his clothes on" and his usual big grin.

As the captains listened they argued one point. The *Hartford* should not lead the wooden ships. The *Brooklyn* had heavier chase guns; she had a sort of cow-catcher device for picking up torpedoes. The *Brooklyn* should lead the way!

Finally Glasgow agreed. Then he hammered home one point. No ship must stop. The channel was too narrow. If a ship stopped she would block the ships behind her.

The captains could see the point. They agreed that going in on flood tide would help them through.

"A red buoy marks the eastern end of the torpedoes. Keep to starboard of it. You'll be under the guns of Fort Morgan but not over the torpedoes." Glasgow got up, smiling. "That's all, gentlemen." He shook hands with each captain as they went out.

Young Captain Perkins lingered. "Have you a few minutes, sir?"

"Always!" Glasgow smiled at him. "It would be a shame to cut short your call when you 'have all your clothes on,' wouldn't it?"

It was good to hear that hearty laugh ring out. Not many of his captains had hearty laughs these

255

days. He couldn't blame them. The last seven
months had been enough to wring any sense of
humor dry.

His quartermaster on duty reported that the
Tecumseh had arrived. Glasgow went to call on
her captain and to brief him on maneuvers for the
next morning.

Back in his cabin alone, he sat down to write
two letters. First to Loyall:

> *. . . I have been devoted to you both. . . .*
> *Take care of your mother if I should go, and*
> *may God bless and protect you both. . . .*

Then he wrote to Virginia. It might be, he
knew, his last letter to her:

> *My dearest wife,*
> *I write and leave this letter for you. I am*
> *going into Mobile Bay in the morning, "if*
> *God is my leader," and I hope He is, and in*
> *Him I place my trust. If He thinks it is the*
> *proper time for me to die I am ready to sub-*
> *mit to His will. . . .*

The next morning the fleet was under way, the
monitors starting first because they were slower,
the other ships lashed in pairs, with the *Brooklyn*
leading. Glasgow scowled at that decision; it did
make sense, the *Brooklyn*'s chase guns *were* heavier, but he still didn't like it!

At dawn they hoisted flags. Glasgow looked up. A south wind. Good. It would help clear the smoke.

But when the battle became a thunderous din, smoke hid the vessels ahead of the *Hartford*. Glasgow climbed into the port main rigging to see over the smoke—higher and higher until he was holding onto the futtock shrouds. Quartermaster Knowles came up beside him.

"What is it?" Glasgow yelled.

Mr. Knowles had a piece of line. "To secure you to the rigging, sir! If you were wounded and fell . . ."

"Nonsense! I'm all right!"

"Captain's orders, sir."

And a captain was in command of his own ship. Glasgow looked down at Captain Drayton standing below, watching. He shrugged and submitted. Mr. Knowles secured him, then returned to the deck.

Lashed to the rigging, Glasgow stood above the smoke, in the crashing roar of the battle, watching the action. The monitors—slow—but they were moving right along. There was the ironclad *Tennessee*, just beyond the torpedoes, waiting to attack.

The *Chickasaw* was getting off two shots to one for the other monitors. That Perkins was a . . . Then he saw Perkins standing on the top of his forward turret, exposed to every shot from Fort Morgan.

He roared down to Captain Drayton. That young fool Perkins was on top of a turret. Was there any way to signal the *Chickasaw* and order him to go below where he belonged?

No, the captain said, there was no way to signal "the young fool." But he would not be falling from the rigging if he were injured. It was all very correct and polite. The captain even added "Admiral Farragut, sir!" to the end of his remarks.

Glasgow turned back to watching the action. He stiffened. What in the name of sense? The *Brooklyn* was slowing down. She was trying to turn. If she got athwart the channel she would block the whole fleet. She was signaling.

A signalman climbed into the rigging on the foremast. The monitors, he reported, were getting in front of the *Brooklyn* and delaying her. What should she do?

"Go ahead!"

The *Brooklyn* was not obeying. The *Tecumseh*, the leading monitor—he stared, then gasped. She was going too far to port! Beyond the red buoy. If she hit a torpedo . . .

Suddenly water spurted like a geyser; the *Tecumseh* shuddered, lurched, and began to sink.

Glasgow leaned over and shouted to Captain

Jouett in the gunboat *Metacomet* on his port side. "A monitor's sinking! Send a boat to pick up survivors!"

The *Brooklyn* was signaling again.

Glasgow yelled to the leadsman in the port-quarter boat. "Is there water enough to port?"

"Aye, aye, sir!"

He yelled to Captain Drayton. "Take the lead! Pass the *Brooklyn!*"

The *Metacomet* backed, swinging the *Hartford* to port.

The signalman reported. "The *Brooklyn* says there are torpedoes ahead, sir."

"Damn the torpedoes! Go ahead! Four bells, Drayton!" And he yelled down to the *Metacomet*. "Full speed ahead!" Then he swore in all the languages he knew. In that delay under the guns of Fort Morgan he had heard sounds in the smoke below—the thuds of shells, the explosions, the splintering crashes, the rumble of dislodged guns careening across the deck. Death might or might not strike from the torpedoes below them. It was certainly striking from the guns of Fort Morgan.

Straight over the torpedoes the *Hartford* led the way and the other ships followed. But no more torpedoes exploded.

They passed Fort Morgan and confronted the *Tennessee* and her gunboat escort. In vain they poured broadsides into her. The shot rattled off her casemates. In vain they rammed her, bows on, at top speed. The wooden ships came out of the collisions with damaged bows.

Finally the *Tennessee*, apparently unscathed, withdrew to shoal waters near Fort Morgan, where their deep-draft vessels could not reach her.

The wooden fleet came to anchor. The stewards got breakfast under way. Surgeon Palmer called for a launch to take him from ship to ship, checking the casualties.

A lookout on the *Hartford* yelled a warning. The *Tennessee* was coming out again! Making straight for them!

Drums beat to quarters.

Glasgow hailed Surgeon Palmer as he left the *Hartford* on his launch. "Hail Perkins of the *Chickasaw*! Tell him to take the *Tennessee*!"

The rams were east of the *Tennessee*. The Southern ironclad would reach his wooden ships before the monitors could overtake her. Until the monitors came up, his ships must bear the brunt. He signaled them. Hit her bows on, full speed! Those who had not been too disabled in the earlier action began the fight.

Presently the *Chickasaw* caught up with the *Tennessee*. The monitor came up on her stern and stuck like a leech, slamming one shot after another into the ram.

At last the *Tennessee* surrendered. One ironclad ram had withstood a fleet. They had finally conquered, but they had paid a fearful price.

Surgeon Palmer reported back from his rounds. On the wooden vessels 52 killed and 170 wounded.

Almost half the dead were on the *Hartford*. Glasgow stood by the row of bodies on the deck. He uncovered his head and did not know at first that tears were running down his face.

Surgeon Palmer finished his report: When the *Tecumseh* went down, 93 died, only 21 survived.

"What of the other monitors?" Glasgow asked.

"No casualties, Admiral. If the *Tecumseh* had not got off course and struck a mine, it looks as though there would have been no casualties on the monitors."

Ericsson's words crawled through his mind again. "*Handsome coffins.*"

The morning after the battle young Perkins came to talk to his admiral. "Have you a few minutes, sir?"

"All the time in the world!" Glasgow told him.

Young Perkins was not laughing this morning. He told of the heroism of Captain Craven on the *Tecumseh*. "You remember, sir, the pilot house was atop the turret. Just a narrow hatchway out of

261

it. Captain Craven was there with his pilot. When the *Tecumseh* was struck, both men turned to the hatchway. Captain Craven said, 'After you, pilot. I leave my ship last.' He didn't get out."

The next thing Glasgow knew he was stretched out on a table, with young Perkins and Surgeon Palmer staring down at him.

"What's going on?"

"You—you fainted, sir!" Captain Perkins said. "I—I thought for a minute you were dead!"

"Nonsense. I'm just tired." He started to sit up.

"Lie still!" Surgeon Palmer did not even add "sir."

"C-can I help do anything?" Captain Perkins asked.

"No, thank you. I'll manage all right."

"Then I'll . . . good morning, sir."

"And you needn't say anything about this," Glasgow told him. "No use getting anybody upset."

"Aye, aye, sir. I'm—I'm upset enough for everybody!" He tiptoed out.

"A fine lad!" Glasgow said.

Surgeon Palmer stared in silence. Then he said, "Admiral Farragut, I'm not going to mince words. I think you are the kind who can stand the truth. I think you deserve to know it."

Glasgow mustered a smile. "You look almost as solemn as young Perkins!"

The doctor did not smile. "Admiral, I've had occasion to tell a man sometimes that time was running out. Sometimes I have said to a man 'If you knew you had only six months to live, what would you do with it?' A man who is strong enough to face it can make those last six months the richest days of his life."

"You're not telling me I have only six months?"

"No. I don't know how long. Six days, six weeks, six months, six years. But—time is running out. So—plan your life from now on. Say to yourself 'If I have only today—tomorrow—this month— what do I want to do with it?' "

22. *"EL GRAN ALMIRANTE"*

It was very still in the cabin. Finally Glasgow said, "Time running out . . . My wish would be a rather mixed-up one. If I knew time was running out, I'd want to serve my country to my last day. But I'd also want to spend all the time I could with my wife. I'd want to make up to her for all the grief and worry of these last years. Navy duty and time with a man's wife, they don't always go together very well, do they?" Then, after a pause, he said sternly, "And I want this talk to come under the head of classified information! Is that clear?"

"Aye, aye, sir."

New orders from Washington: Admiral Farragut would be detached from duty in Mobile Bay; he would take charge of the North Atlantic

Squadron and lay siege to Wilmington, North Carolina.

"Out of the question!" Surgeon Palmer said. "If you collapsed in the middle of the action, you'd make a hash of it."

It was a hard letter to write. Glasgow admitted he was very tired. Finally—even telegrams could take forever to reach the Gulf stations—new orders came. Admiral Farragut would take the *Hartford* back to New York and go on furlough.

At last! he thought. Some time to rest!

Before the *Hartford* came to anchor in New York a boat brought dignitaries to greet Admiral Farragut. New York wanted to honor him.

Virginia was waiting for him at a hotel. "Darling, you look so tired!"

"Just a little," he said.

Parades, handshaking, cheering crowds, banquets and speeches—long speeches. But Virginia was with him. Her eyes were glowing at the praise they heaped on him.

At last they were home in Hastings. "I hope I don't have to be honored anymore!" he said.

Congress voted a new rank—Vice-Admiral. He must go to Washington to be honored. More crowds, more banquets, more handshaking, more speeches—long speeches. But Virginia was with him.

Back to New York and more honoring to be

done. New York invited him to become a citizen of their fair metropolis. They gave him a gift of fifty thousand dollars to buy a home and help maintain it.

In April of 1865 the war's end and more celebrations. Their greatest naval hero must ride in the victory parades. On the heels of joy—tragedy with the death of Lincoln.

A telegram called Glasgow to Washington to be one of the pallbearers.

Virginia wept over the death of Lincoln. "It's not fair! It's not *fair*! To go through all he did to save the Union—and then to die so soon!"

Glasgow did not try to answer.

The summer of 1866 another summons to Washington. Congress had voted the rank of Admiral of the Navy and immediately awarded the rank to Admiral Farragut.

"We can rest after this," he told Virginia. "There is nothing else that can happen."

But soon he was called to Washington again by a very troubled President Johnson. The President was worried about the bitterness in the North, the vindictiveness of some leaders. He wanted to make a swing through the main cities to talk to the people, to urge them to remember Lincoln's words: ". . . with malice toward none, with charity for all . . ."

The President wanted their leaders to go with him. Would Admiral Farragut go?

I cannot refuse this, Glasgow thought. He said, "If my wife can go with me. We have been apart too long."

"Of course, Admiral Farragut!"

The tour was sometimes heartwarming and sometimes shocking: heartwarming when people cheered their heroes and listened to their President, shocking when people rioted and yelled curses.

"I'd rather go through the Red River blockade again!" Glasgow said when the tour was over. "God help President Johnson. Winning the peace is going to be harder than winning the war."

It was restful in their home in New York City. Stacks of correspondence but Glasgow had a secretary to help him; too many invitations but Virginia was always with him.

A good way to live! he thought. Thinking—"if this is the only day."

The spring of 1867 new orders came. Glasgow wanted to shout "No, no! Don't send me!" But he could not.

Admiral of the Navy Farragut would take command of the European Squadron, on a cruise to pay courtesy calls on all overseas capitals. He would be gone a year or two; his flagship would be the new steam frigate, *Franklin*, four thousand tons, Captain Pennock commanding, Surgeon-General Foltz on his staff.

Virginia glowed at the news. "How wonderful. I can just see them cheering for you everywhere!"

But you can't see them cheering, he thought. You can't be with me. *No woman can be aboard a man-of-war on duty*. He said, "Yes, they'll cheer me, dear. Because I'm the head of the most powerful navy in the world."

"And to have two good friends with you!"

Captain Pennock was married to Virginia's cousin, Margaret; Surgeon-General Foltz had been with the *Hartford* at New Orleans.

"Yes, that's fine, dear," Glasgow said.

"You don't *sound* very happy."

"I'm just wishing you could go along. But of course that's impossible."

"I'll book passage to Europe and meet you there," she said. "And I'm sure Margaret will come with me. Even if we can't be together on shipboard, Margaret and I can join you in ports."

He smothered a feeling of panic and said, "Just fine."

Virginia cocked her head and looked at him intently. "Something's on your mind."

"I'm just selfish. I enjoy being with you."

Two days before the *Franklin* was to sail word

came from Washington: Mrs. Farragut and Mrs. Pennock would sail with their husbands on the *Franklin*.

Glasgow was so happy he could not keep his voice from shaking when he told Virginia.

"Darling, what is it?" she asked. "What's wrong?"

"We've been apart too much."

"But that's all over now. We'll have the rest of our lives together."

He mustered a smile. "Of course. Silly of me, isn't it?"

June 28 the *Franklin* sailed. The Fourth of July they celebrated. The next day they celebrated their admiral's sixty-sixth birthday with even more fanfare.

"Sixty-six years young!" was the favorite toast.

After the dinner Surgeon Foltz asked, "Do you have a few minutes to spare, Admiral?"

"All the time in . . . Of course, Surgeon Foltz."

In his cabin Surgeon Foltz sat a moment, rubbing his chin. Then he said, "I talked with Surgeon Palmer after Mobile Bay."

"That so?"

"Doctors often exchange classified information."

"You're not going to stew over what he said, are you?" Glasgow asked. "You aren't going to tell me to 'slow down' or 'take it easier'—all that sort of thing?"

"No, Admiral Farragut. Before you could slow down we'd have to send you to be redesigned—like a ship being razeed, or whatever. Just carry on. Live your days the way they mean the most to you. If you ever want to consult me, I'm here. Anything we say will be classified information."

"Thank you!"

"Carry on, Admiral!"

The triumphant tour began in Paris, and went on from there to one capital after another. Everywhere the *Franklin* stopped the Admiral of the Fleet was honored with salutes, receptions, dinners, and speeches—long speeches. He was entertained by the heads of states, by presidents, princes, emperors, and kings.

His officers accompanied their admiral with a mixture of pride and despair: pride at all the honors heaped on him, pride that he could talk to so many men in their own languages; despair when they tried to pry him loose from studying harbors, fortifications, new ships, and the latest guns, to get him from things military to the next reception or banquet on time.

His secretaries tried to catch "a watch below" before evening. They soon learned they would be on duty after midnight till the small hours of the morning. No matter how late the Admiral returned from a banquet or reception he always wanted to dictate his observations on anything military he'd seen that day.

Please, the secretaries would beg, the Admiral must be tired! Couldn't these notes wait until tomorrow? But their Admiral always insisted he wanted to dictate "while things were fresh in his mind."

One night very late Surgeon Foltz came to the Admiral's cabin.

A weary secretary appealed to him. "Sir, can't you persuade the Admiral to take it a little easier? Tell him tomorrow is another day?"

Surgeon Foltz cocked an eyebrow. "You youngsters aren't getting soft, are you?"

The young man flushed. "I'm just thinking of the Admiral, sir! I don't want him to—well—overdo."

Surgeon Foltz grinned. "It's too late to turn our Admiral in for remodeling. We'll just have to put up with him as he is."

"Yes, sir." The secretary sighed and picked up his pencil again. "I'm ready, sir."

The endless round of visits continued.

At Christmastime the *Franklin* was on anchor at Port Mahon at the Island of Minorca.

271

A group of natives came aboard. They wanted to speak to "*El Gran Almirante.*" They addressed him in careful English. Glasgow answered them in Spanish.

They beamed. They were from Ciudadella, they said. The birthplace of *El Gran Almirante*'s father. The citizens of Ciudadella wished to honor him.

The day after Christmas, Glasgow, Virginia, the Pennocks, and some officers from the *Franklin* set out to drive to Ciudadella. The whole island must have been alerted. Crowds lined every mile of the way, waving and cheering.

Outside the city the alcalde and a procession waited. A fine big barouche for *El Gran Almirante* and his wife. They rode at the head of the procession into the city. People jammed the roads, crowded on balconies, and perched on rooftops.

The barouche stopped in front of a mansion. The crowd was so dense that laughing policemen had to clear a path to the door.

It was midnight before the crowd dispersed. At dawn they were back again.

The alcalde came to take *El Gran Almirante* on a tour—just a very short tour—of the city. The tour moved at a snail's pace through the cheering crowds.

The alcalde presented Glasgow with two treasures: a book with the registry of his father's birth,

272

a copy of a law passed that morning—*El Gran Almirante Farragut* was now an honorary citizen of Ciudadella.

"I don't know what it is," Virginia said, "but it seems to me this is the loveliest time of all."

"This," Glasgow told her, "is a button-bustin' occasion."

She raised a quizzical eyebrow. "I'm sure that means something."

"It's a long story," he said. "A very long story. Back to 1807, when I was going-on-six."

Format by Sue Crooks
Set in 12/15 Janson
Composed by The Haddon Craftsmen, Inc.
Printed by The Murray Printing Company
Bound by The Haddon Craftsmen, Inc.
HARPER & ROW, PUBLISHERS, INCORPORATED